ST. BARTHOLOMEW SCHOOL

Lynnette

THE NEW CATHEDRAL BASIC READERS

CURRICULUM FOUNDATION SERIES

REG. U.S. PAT. OFF.

THE NEW
More Friends and Neighbors

CATHEDRAL EDITION

The Reverend John A. O'Brien

A revision of THE NEW More Friends and Neighbors
William S. Gray, A. Sterl Artley, and May Hill Arbuthnot

SCOTT, FORESMAN AND COMPANY

Chicago Atlanta Dallas Palo Alto Fair Lawn, N. J.

Stories

Oak Hill Neighbors

Copyright, 1954, by Scott, Foresman and Company.
Previous Copyright, 1947, 1942, by Scott, Foresman and Company.
Philippines Copyright, 1954, by Scott, Foresman and Company.
Printed in the United States of America. International rights reserved.
With Ecclesiastical Approval. Chicago, September 2, 1953.

3

Oak Hill Neighbors

A Horse for Bobby

"Hello, Mr. Little," called Bobby Wells as he waved to his neighbor.

"I have a new horse!"

"You have?" said Mr. Little.

"Yes! It's in our back yard," said Bobby.

"When did you get your new horse?" asked Mr. Little.

"Just today," said Bobby. "Father says it's a good horse for me. He says it's the best horse on Oak Street."

From *Rowena Carey*, by Ruth Langland Holberg.
Copyright, 1949, by Ruth Langland Holberg,
reprinted by permission of Doubleday & Company, Inc.

6

"Is it a little horse about this high?"
asked Mr. Little.

"Oh, no!" said Bobby. "It's bigger
than that. It's a big, big horse.

It's the biggest horse you ever saw.
It's two times as high as you are."

Suddenly Mr. Little laughed. He said,
"That's a big horse for a little boy."

Bobby did not answer because just then
Mr. Little went into his house.

Before long Bobby saw Nancy and
Tom Winters coming home from school.

He waved and called, "I have a horse!
It's the biggest horse you ever saw.
It's two times as high as Mr. Little."

"That's a pretty big horse," said Tom.

"Well," said Bobby, "maybe it's not
two times as big as Mr. Little. But it's
as big as he is. And it has horns."

"Horns!" laughed Nancy. "Your horse
must be a cow. Cows have horns, but
horses don't."

Bobby did not answer Nancy because
Patty Little came along just then.

"Oh, Patty!" shouted Bobby. "I have
a new horse. It's the biggest horse
you ever saw. And it has big horns.
It hasn't any legs, but it can gallop."

"Why, Bobby Wells!" said Patty.
"There isn't a horse anywhere that
can gallop without legs."

Bobby did not answer because he saw
his brother and sister coming.

Bobby waved and shouted, "Come on,
Peter and Ann. Come and see my horse."

9

"What a horse!" laughed Peter.

"It's as big as Mr. Little," said Tom.

"It has horns. But it isn't a cow," shouted Nancy.

"It is a horse that can gallop without legs," cried Patty. "And it's right here on Oak Street."

Bobby did not say anything. He just galloped on his big, high horse.

Patty Helps Herself

"Whatever are you doing, Father?" called Patty. "Why are you watering the garden in wintertime?"

"I thought you would like to try your new ice skates," said Mr. Little. "Now can you guess what I'm doing?"

"Oh, yes!" said Patty. "The water will turn to ice. I can skate tomorrow."

"Not tomorrow," said Patty's father. "I'll have to put on more water then. You must wait until Saturday."

At breakfast on Saturday morning, Patty cried, "I can skate today!"

"You can try," said her mother with a smile.

Right after breakfast Patty and her mother went out to the garden.

Patty put on her skates in a hurry.

"Here I go!" she cried. But her feet suddenly flew up, and she sat down.

Mrs. Little helped her up, but Patty fell right down again.

"I can't skate," cried Patty. "I can't stand up!"

Just then Peter Wells waved and called, "I'll help Patty skate."

"Oh, fine! Maybe you can pull her across the ice," said Mrs. Little.

Peter pulled Patty across the ice again and again.

"Put one foot in front of the other," he told Patty. "Push your feet along."

"I can't!" cried Patty. "My feet want to go everywhere but in front of me."

"I think you're doing fine," Peter said. "I'll come and help you again tomorrow."

At lunch Patty's father asked,
"Did you skate today?"

"No!" said Patty. "I just sat down.
But Peter is trying to help me. He is
going to help me again tomorrow."

Father smiled and said, "I know how
a girl can help herself. Maybe you will
find a way to do it after lunch."

Patty was surprised when she went
to skate after lunch.

She saw a long clothesline
across one end of the garden.
It went right over the ice.

14

Patty put on her skates and tried
to stand up on the ice. But her feet
started to fly out from under her.

Then her hands found the clothesline!

"Oh!" laughed Patty. "Father put
the line across the ice to help me."

With both hands on the clothesline,
Patty began to push her feet along.
First one foot, then the other foot.

Before long Patty could skate with
just one hand on the line. Soon she was
flying along with both hands off the line.

At last she had helped herself.

Fun on the Ice

One Saturday morning there was ice behind the barn at Oak Tree Farm.

The three Winters children were happy. Today they could skate. Some friends were coming to skate with them.

"It soon will be lunchtime," said Tom. "I wish our friends would hurry."

"I wish they would, too," said Nancy.

"Me, too!" puffed little Jack.

His legs were going fast, but his arms were going faster as he tried to keep up.

Suddenly Tom saw his pet calf running
out on the ice. Tom waved his arms
and shouted, "Get off the ice, Spot!
Go back before you get hurt!"

The calf's feet were starting to slide
out from under her.

One front foot went this way, and
one back foot went that way.

Down she sat with a big bump.

Tom skated over to Spot, and so did
Jack and Nancy. They put their arms
around the calf and helped her stand up.

All at once the calf's feet went out
from under her. Down she sat again!

Down sat the children, too!

Arms and legs waved and wiggled.

Just then Peter and Ann and Patty
came with their skates.

"What are you doing?" called Peter
with a big smile. "Are you trying
to get that calf to skate?"

"No! I'm trying to get her off the ice
before she hurts herself," said Tom.

"Oh!" said Patty. "Spot skates like
I did at first. She just sits down!
Peter helped me, and he can help Spot."

"I pulled you," Peter said to Patty.
"But I don't think I can pull Spot."

"Oh, no!" laughed Tom. "But all
of us together can push Spot off the ice.
Then she won't fall and get hurt."

The next thing Spot knew, she was
starting to slide over the ice.

She was not hurt, but she was scared.

"M-a-a!" she said as she went sliding
across the ice. "M-a-a! M-a-a!"

19

Fun in the Snow

Oak Hill was in the park at the end
of Oak Street. It was a fine place
to slide in the wintertime.

Right after lunch one Saturday
the children came with their sleds.

Up one side of the big hill came Tom
from Oak Tree Farm. Behind him
climbed Jack and Nancy with their sleds.

Up the other side climbed Peter and
Bobby, Ann and Patty.

The children all met at the top
of the hill under the old oak tree.

One by one they jumped on their sleds.

One by one they went sliding down
to the end of the snowy hill.

Then they all walked up.

Again and again the children went
sliding down and walking up.

A quick slide down. A slow walk up.

A long, slow walk through
the soft, wet snow.

Soon Jack and Bobby stopped sliding
and started to make a snow man.

"I'll help," Ann called to the boys.
"Wet snow makes a good snow man."

Nancy came to help, too. And soon
there was a funny snow man on the hill.

"I'll make a hat for him," said Ann.
Just then she found an old round pan
in the deep, wet snow.

"Here is an old pan," she said. "But it
is full of holes. No one can use it."

"I can!" shouted Jack. "I'll use it
for a sled. The holes won't matter."

Swish! Jack went sliding down
in the old round pan.

The pan turned this way and that way.
Suddenly it turned over.

Out went Jack into the deep, wet snow.
But it did not matter. He was not hurt.

"I'm going next," called Nancy as she
ran to pull Jack out of the soft snow.

One after another the children tried
to slide in the funny round sled.

One after another they had to be pulled
out of the soft, wet snow.

"This old pan makes a funny sled,"
said Bobby as he came back up the hill.

Suddenly Ann smiled and took the pan
out of Bobby's arms. She put it on top
of the snow man's head.

"And that's not the end of the pan,"
she said. "It makes a funny hat, too."

"What a funny pan!" laughed Tom.
"First it was a pan. Next it was a sled.
Now it's a hat for a snow man's head!"

Jean's Valentine

As the other children got ready to make
valentines, Jean Waterfield sat thinking.

"I don't know which of my friends
to make a valentine for," she said.

"I like one as well as another."

Betty Fox said, "My valentine is going
to be for Ann. She is my best friend."

Sister smiled and said to Betty,
"You may make a second valentine for Ann
if you like. I'll tell you what I want
you to do with the first one you make."

Sister picked up a little box and said,
"All of your names are in this box.

Each of you may take a little paper
with a name on it. Put that name
on the first valentine that you make.

This way everyone will get a valentine."

"Oh, that will be fun," said Betty.

Sister said, "We give valentines to show
our love. We are all good friends here.
So no matter who gets your valentine,
he will know it is from a friend."

One by one the children went up and
took a paper out of the box.

Jean got Patty Little's name. So she
made a red paper valentine for Patty.
She cut out three angels to put on it.
But there was no room for the third angel.

Suddenly Jean knew what she would do
with the little angel. She began to make
another valentine out of blue paper.

Peter was making a valentine that opened and shut like a book.

One boy made a paper bunny. He fixed the bunny's tail so that when he pushed it, the end of the bunny's nose wiggled.

Patty found some little foxes to cut out. She had Betty's name. So she put one of the little paper foxes on the valentine for Betty Fox.

The children fixed a big box to put the valentines in. They put red paper on the box and fixed the top so that it would open and shut.

At lunchtime Betty said to her brother, "Jean Waterfield made a blue valentine this morning. She wouldn't let me see it. She said it was for her best friend."

"Maybe you are her best friend," said Bill Fox. "You play with her a lot."

"No," said Betty. "But no matter. Maybe Nancy or Ann is her best friend."

After lunch Betty and Bill saw Jean talking to some other children.

Jean said, "I made my second valentine for my best friend. Sister told us to."

"Won't you tell us who it is?" asked Ann.

Jean just shook her head. She would not say another word.

At two o'clock all the children shut
their books and put them away.

Everyone was ready for the party.

One at a time Peter took the valentines
out of the box that the children had fixed.

Sister called out the names.

Every boy and girl in the room went
up to get a valentine. Some of them
went up two or three times.

At last Sister came to a blue valentine
with a little angel on the front.

She saw the words on it. For a minute
she did not say a thing. Then she said,
"Let's ask Jean to put her valentine
where everyone can see it. She has made
it for the One we all love best.

She has made a valentine for Jesus."

Bobby's New Shoes

"I wish I had shoes like Peter's,"
said Bobby one morning. "I wish I had
some shoes with big high tops."

"I must have my shoe now," said Peter.
"I'll be late for school if I don't hurry."

"Bobby must have new shoes soon,"
said Mother. "We will buy them today."

Right after lunch they went downtown,
and Mother bought new shoes for Bobby.

"Now!" said Bobby. "I have shoes
with big high tops like Peter's."

"I must have new shoes," said Mother.

The man opened and shut box after box of shoes. Mother tried on shoes, and Bobby waited. He sat and sat and sat.

Suddenly Bobby could not sit and wait for his mother any more.

His big high shoes started making big high steps. Away they walked with Bobby's feet inside them.

Left foot up! Right foot down!

Big high steps!

Left, right! Left, right!

Big high steps across the floor!

Bobby walked right out of the store.

Left, right stepped the new shoes along the sidewalk. Left, right! Left, right!

Bobby came to the end of the walk and turned the corner. Then he began to count his steps.

"One, two! One, two!" he counted.

He turned corner after corner, but he did not count the corners.

Soon Bobby and his fine new shoes came to the corner of a busy street.

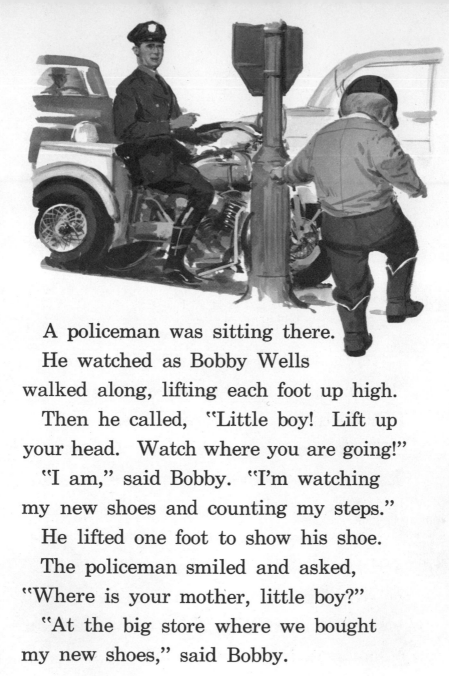

A policeman was sitting there.
He watched as Bobby Wells
walked along, lifting each foot up high.

Then he called, "Little boy! Lift up
your head. Watch where you are going!"

"I am," said Bobby. "I'm watching
my new shoes and counting my steps."

He lifted one foot to show his shoe.

The policeman smiled and asked,
"Where is your mother, little boy?"

"At the big store where we bought
my new shoes," said Bobby.

Suddenly Bobby looked around.

"I don't know where I am," he said.

Bobby was lost, but it did not matter. He knew that the policeman would not let anything happen to him.

"We can soon fix that," the policeman said. "What's the name of the store where you bought the shoes?"

"I don't know," said Bobby.

All at once a funny thing happened. Without a word, the policeman lifted Bobby right up in front of him.

Then another funny thing happened. The policeman took off Bobby's shoe.

"Oh, don't take my shoe," Bobby said.

The policeman looked inside the shoe and read the words "Bell's Shoe Store."

"Now I know where your mother bought your new shoes," laughed the policeman. "That's where we will go."

Off went the policeman with Bobby
riding in front. They went riding down
the street, riding around the corners,
riding to the big shoe store!

Bobby's mother was there in front
of the store, looking for him.

"God bless you, dear!" she cried.
"How did you happen to run away?"

The big policeman smiled as he lifted
Bobby down. Then he said, "Bobby didn't
run away. That isn't what happened.

Those fine new shoes that you bought
for Bobby just ran away with him."

Which Circus?

A big circus was coming to town!
It was coming next week, and that
made John Day very happy.

He had saved enough money to pay
his own way into the circus.
That made him happy, too.

But there was something that made
John more happy than that. He and
his father would see the circus together.

Circus pictures were everywhere!

Every circus sign had large pictures
of animals and clowns.

Pictures of big yellow lions!

Pictures of elephants and bears!

Pictures of big fat clowns!

Pictures of funny little clowns!

When John shut his eyes, he could see
those elephants and clowns doing tricks.

"I'm glad that circus day comes
at the end of next week," he thought.
"I couldn't wait more than a week."

Just then John heard someone calling.

"Come to the circus with us, John," called Bill Fox.

"It isn't until next week," said John.

"Oh!" said Peter. "Bill isn't talking about the big circus. We are going to the little circus that came last night."

"I saved my dimes for the big circus," said John. "It has elephants and clowns."

"But it won't have a merry-go-round," said Bill. "This little show has one, and we're going to ride on it now."

John did not say a word for a minute.

At last he said, "I guess I won't go. I'll wait for the real circus next week."

John watched as his friends ran off. Then he heard the merry-go-round, and he knew that he wanted to ride on it.

John took his money out of his pocket. He looked at all the dimes he had saved. Suddenly he ran after Peter and Bill.

At the big merry-go-round John paid
a dime and went riding with his friends.

He paid another dime and went riding
once more. He paid a dime for a balloon.
Then he saw the boys go into the show.

John counted the dimes he had left.

"I have enough money for this show,"
John thought. "I'll go to it. A week is
a long while to wait for the real circus."

So he paid his money and went inside.

A pony was jumping. Dogs were
doing tricks that made John laugh.

Soon John stopped laughing.

There was just one clown in the show.

There were no elephants or bears.

John was not happy as he walked home.
When he got there, he told his father
about the merry-go-round and the show.

"Oh, the real circus does not come
until next week," his father said.
"That was just a dog and pony show."

"I know," said John. "I'm sorry I
didn't save my money for the real circus.
I wanted to go with you."

John's father smiled at him and said,
"We can see the circus train come in.

We can see the elephants and bears
and lions come off the train. We can
see them parade to the circus ground.

That won't take any money at all."

"Good!" said John. "Maybe a parade
will be as much fun as the real circus!"

Ellen Keeps Lent

"Good morning, Father," said Ellen Day. "Can you help me? I'm trying to think of a good way to keep Lent.

I want to do something big this Lent."

"That's fine, Ellen!" said the priest.

"I'm glad you came to see me. I have a letter here about a little girl who never has enough to eat. Would you be willing to help her?"

"Oh, yes, Father," answered Ellen.

"The girl's name is May Sun," said
the priest. "She lives far away.

Here is May Sun's picture. If you
want to be her friend, you may have it."

"Oh, thank you, Father," cried Ellen.

The priest said, "This hungry girl
walks a long way every day to a Mission.
She wants to find out all she can
about Jesus and Blessed Mother."

"But, Father, how can I give May Sun
things to eat?" asked Ellen.

"You can give money to the Mission,"
answered Father White. "The priest
at the Mission Station is kind and
good. He will buy food for May."

"How can I get money?" asked Ellen.

"Well," said the priest, "maybe you
could give up candy and shows."

"I could do that for Lent," cried Ellen.

"That's a good way to keep Lent!"

When Ellen got home, she cut a hole
in a candy box and put in some pennies.

"This is for you, May Sun," she said.
"All through Lent I'll bring money to buy
food for you at the Mission Station!"

Ellen told her mother about May Sun.

"She is always hungry," said Ellen.
"But she walks to the Mission Station
every day. She does it because she wants
to hear about Jesus and Blessed Mother.

I won't go to picture shows in Lent or
buy any candy until after Good Friday.
And if I say a prayer, maybe God will
help me get more money for May."

All through Lent Ellen saved her money.

Each day she would bring whatever she had saved and put it in her little box for the Mission Station.

Near the end of Lent, Ellen's mother said to her, "Easter will be here soon. Today we must buy you an Easter hat,"

Ellen loved to get new Easter clothes. She loved to go downtown with Mother.

Soon they were downtown and Ellen was looking in a big store window.

"Oh!" she cried. "There is the hat I want. The one with the blue flowers."

They went inside the store and Ellen
tried on the hat.

"Oh! It's beautiful," she said.

"How does it look on me?"

Ellen stood and looked at herself
for a while. Then she said slowly,
"I'm not going to take this hat.

My old hat will do for Easter.

Could you please give me the money
you would have paid for this hat?"

"Why, Ellen, what for?" asked Mother.

Ellen said, "I want lots of money
for that Mission Station. I don't want
May Sun ever to be hungry again!"

"Very well, Ellen, if that is what
you want to do," said her mother.

Ellen said, "It won't hurt me to go
without a new hat. But it must hurt
May Sun not to have enough to eat!"

Mother smiled, and they went home.

When Ellen got up on Easter morning she saw something near her Mission box.

It was a hat with blue flowers!

"Why! It's the hat I saw downtown," she cried. "I wonder when Mother got it."

Then she saw a letter. Slowly she read the words. "This is not a new hat, Ellen. I have made your old hat look like the one you wanted. Happy Easter! Mother."

Ellen put on the hat. "Oh! It does look nice on me, doesn't it, May Sun?

What a happy Easter I will have!"

A Trick for Wags

Molly Good was trying to get her dog to do a trick. Molly would roll a ball and say, "Bring the ball here, Wags! Bring the ball to me."

Sometimes Wags would bring the ball to Molly, but sometimes he just stood.

Once in a while he would look around as if he did not hear Molly at all.

Bill and Betty were watching. Bill said, "I know a good trick for dogs. I saw it at the dog and pony show last spring."

Bill told Molly about the dog that had skated on four roller skates.

"I wonder if a dog could skate on just two roller skates," said Bill.

Molly ran and got her roller skates.

It took the children a long while to get Wags on them.

At last he stood with his front feet on the roller skates. Then Molly began to pull him along the walk.

But Wags sat down. Just his skates rolled along behind Molly.

Wags barked and barked at the skates.

"Quiet, Wags!" said Molly. "Be quiet. Everyone in town will hear you bark."

After a while Wags stopped barking.

Then Betty said, "I wonder how we can keep the roller skates on Wags."

"I know!" cried Molly. "I'll tie them."

Soon the roller skates were tied on.

Betty pushed Wags as Molly pulled.

Suddenly Betty fell, and Wags jumped.

The skates stayed on, but the dog's feet wiggled this way and wiggled that way.

Wags began to bark again.

After the children had rested a minute,
Bill shouted, "I know what to do!

Molly can pull Wags. Betty can push.
And I'll keep him from falling."

Slowly they went along the sidewalk.

Now Wags could roller skate!

But he skated with two feet rolling,
and two feet running to keep up!

As Wags skated faster and faster,
Bill cried, "He's a real trick dog!

If he had skates of his own, we could
all skate together this summer."

Tom's Wish

Tom Winters sat on the back steps
and looked over the quiet farmyard.

School was out, and it was time
for summer work on the farm.

"I don't like farms in the summer,"
Tom thought. "I don't like to hoe weeds.

Hoe weeds! Hoe weeds! That's all I do
in the summer. I wish I never had to hoe
another weed. Fishing is lots more fun."

Tom was so busy thinking that he
did not hear his father come outside.

Father said, "I have news for you, Tom. Uncle Dick has gone to the city to buy things for his store at Four Corners.

He will be gone two days.

He wants you to stay at the store with Aunt Sally while he is away."

For a minute Tom wondered if he could be hearing right.

Then he stood up and said, "Boy! No weeds for two days. Let's go!"

When they got to the country store, Aunt Sally and her cat were resting.

"I'm glad you came to visit," she said.

After Tom's father left, Aunt Sally said,
"I'll rest for ten more minutes, Tom.
You look around if you want to."

Tom wanted to do more than just look.

He wanted to sniff the good smells
in the store.

So he started to walk around.

He hurried right past the chicken feed
and the hoes and rakes and shovels.

He hurried past potatoes and cabbages.

He stopped to sniff some red apples.

Then he began to walk slowly past
the cakes and the cookies. They looked
very good, and they smelled wonderful.
So Tom stood there for a long time.

At last he came to the candy, and
there he saw an ice cream sign.

"Oh!" thought Tom. "I didn't know
that Uncle Dick's store had ice cream
this summer!"

"Now!" said Aunt Sally as she put the cat down. "I have been resting long enough. I must get busy."

"Can I help you?" Tom asked.

"Working in this store would be fun."

"Yes," said his aunt. "You can bring me some cans of corn."

Then she smiled to herself.

"Anyone who works here and helps me may eat anything he wants," she said. "And he may eat as much as he wants."

For the second time that day Tom wondered if he could be hearing right.

"Boy!" he thought. "This is nice work! I can eat while I work. I can eat all the candy and ice cream I want. And I don't have to pay for them with pennies! This is more fun than fishing!"

Tom ate nut cookies while he brought the corn to Aunt Sally.

He ate candy while he cleaned the floor.

He ate ice cream only while he rested.

Tom ate all day. But he did not eat much of the dinner Aunt Sally fixed.

"Thanks," he said. "I'll eat tomorrow while I work and while I rest."

But next day he did not want candy. He did not want cookies or ice cream. He did not want lunch when it was ready.

Soon Uncle Dick came from the city, and Mrs. Winters came to get Tom.

On the drive home he was very quiet.

When he got there, he walked slowly to the garden. There were lots of weeds in the potatoes. So he started hoeing.

He hoed all around the potatoes.

After a while Nancy called, "Dinner!"

"Dinner so soon?" Tom said to himself. "But now that I think of it, I'm hungry."

"Coming!" he called, dropping his hoe. "Save lots of everything for me. I'm as hungry as a bear!"

Animal Friends

The Blessing of the Animals

Every year Jean and her family came
for an Easter visit with Aunt May.
This year they had started on Good Friday
so that Jean could be here for Saturday.

On Easter Saturday people brought
animals to the Old Mission Church.

The priest there blessed the animals
so that all would go well with them
through the year.

Jean had sat under a tree all morning.

She had been waiting for the sound
of bells from the Old Mission Church.

When at last Jean heard the sound
of bells, she jumped up.

She knew that it would soon be time
for the Blessing of the Animals.

Jean thought, "Now at last I can do
what I've wanted to do for so long."

She ran past the tree and into the house.

"Come, little ones," she said as she
picked up Aunt May's lovebirds. "You and
I will go to the Blessing this year."

She cut some colored paper and put it
on the lovebirds to make them pretty.

"There!" she said. "That may look queer
to you now. But you won't think it's queer
when you see the other animals."

The park where the parade began
each year was a busy place. Flowers and
pretty colored papers were everywhere.

People met near Saint Joseph's statue.
Each one brought an animal or a bird.

There were goats, rabbits, hens, cats,
dogs, kittens, and all kinds of birds.

A pig named Sandy ran away.

"Sandy, Sandy," cried a boy, as he tried
to drive the grunting pig back.

"Stop that grunting and be quiet."

Now it was time to start to church.

A man with a brick-red cow went first.
As the children fell in line behind him
all the animals but Sandy were quiet.
And Sandy only grunted now and then.

Slowly the parade went down the street.
People watched from windows and
doorways as it went past. Sometimes they
pointed to this animal or that one.

They smiled often, but they did not talk.

From the steps of the church the priest
blessed the animals as they went past.
Over each one he said a prayer,
    "Bless, O God, this animal
    so that all goes well with it."
"It will be too bad if my birds talk,"
thought Jean. But they were as good as
angels while the priest blessed them.

Sandy wasn't like an angel at all.
The little pig grunted and grunted. It was
too bad, but Sandy was blessed anyway.

After the Blessing, all the people left
the churchyard with their animals.

They smiled and were happy because
they had been blessed by the priest, too.

Many of them rested in the cool park
near Saint Joseph's statue. They sat and
listened to the sound of the Mission bells.

Children laughed and talked and played
with each other's pets. Then they all
went home to get ready for Easter.

Only the birds that made their nests
near Saint Joseph's statue stayed on.

Soon the flowers that had dropped
in the street were all that was left
of the beautiful Blessing Day.

Friends for a Farmer

"Bob—white! Bob—white!"

"Listen to that bird!" cried Nancy.

"I've been hearing that sound all week,"
Tom said. "What kind of bird is it?"

Big Jim, who worked at Oak Tree Farm,
said, "Listen! It sounds like his name!"

The children were quiet as they listened.

"He's saying 'Bob White,'" Nancy said.
"What does Mr. Bob White look like?"

"There he is now," said Jim, pointing. "I'm glad to see him. He's a real help to farmers. He eats bugs and weed seeds."

"Is his nest in that tree?" asked Tom.

"No," said Big Jim. "A bobwhite hides its nest on the ground."

"That's queer," said Nancy. "Is the nest in that field of hay?"

"Maybe," said Jim. "If it is, I'm afraid I'll run over it tomorrow when I cut and rake the hay. That would be too bad."

"Oh," said Tom, "we will find the nest for you in the morning. Bill and Betty will be here then. They can help us."

Like all good farmers, Tom and Nancy were up early the next morning. But Bill and Betty Fox did not come early.

Tom sat in the cool yard, waiting and wondering why his friends were so late.

At last a car turned into the driveway and honked.

"Hello!" Tom called to the Foxes. "Where have you been all morning?"

"Coming to your house!" said Betty.

"We couldn't take the road that goes past the park. There was a bad place in it. We came to a detour sign, and Mother had to take another road."

"That's right," said Bill. "The detour was longer than the other road. So it took us longer to get here."

"Too bad," said Tom. "But you're just in time. Nancy and I are going to find a bobwhite's nest in the hayfield."

On the way to the hayfield Tom told
Bill and Betty about the bobwhites.

"They are a farmer's friends," he said.
"They eat weed seeds and lots of bugs.
Bugs in fields! And bugs in gardens!"

While the children were looking for
the nest, they heard some queer cries.

"Quit, quit! Quit, quit!"

Tom pointed to a bobwhite flying
near the ground.

"That's the mother bird!" he said.
"She's making all those queer cries!

Jim says that a bobwhite often cries
like that. She's only making those cries
to keep us from going near her nest."

Just then Nancy cried, "Here is
the nest! It is full of eggs! We must
show Jim where they are!"

"We must not wait here," said Tom.
"That bird won't quit making those cries
and fly back to her nest until we leave."

Bill said, "If we go far, we may
miss Jim when he comes to the field."

"I know!" said Betty. "Let's put
a sign here for Jim. A detour sign!"

"Fine!" said Tom. "I'll get the wood."

"I'll get some paint," said Nancy.

Bill said, "I'll put the word DETOUR
on the sign in big letters. You have to
have DETOUR on a detour sign."

Jim was cutting the hay by the fence when he saw the detour sign.

"That's queer," he thought. "I've never seen a detour sign in a hayfield before."

Jim quit working and walked quickly to the sign. Then he laughed.

"Well!" he said. "I'll be glad to detour around this nest. Mr. Winters will soon have some new friends to help him by eating bugs and weed seeds."

Jim was right. In only one more week the bobwhite family was eating bugs and weed seeds in the farmer's field.

Sleepy Sam

The days had been getting longer
and longer and hotter and hotter.
Summer had come!

In summer there was one cool spot
at Oak Tree Farm. That cool spot was
under a big tree on top of a hill.

On every hot day old Sleepy Sam
stood there slowly swishing his tail.

Sam was an old horse that had worked
for a long time at the farm. But he had
quit working. He just rested all day long.

One hot day he heard two girls talking.
He swished his tail slowly and listened.

Nancy and her friend from the city were coming up the hill.

When Nancy saw her father near the fence, she waved and pointed to Sam. "May Kitty and I ride Sam?" she called. "Kitty has never tried to ride a horse."

"Where are you going?" asked Father.

"We want to go to Uncle Dick's store at Four Corners," answered Nancy.

Father smiled and said, "Old Sam can take you that far, but not very fast.

The hotter the day, the slower he goes. Don't try to make him trot or gallop."

Quickly Father got the old horse ready
for the girls to ride. Then he pointed
to the highway and said, "Keep off
that road. People drive too fast on it.

Take the sand road through the woods.
It isn't the shortest way to Four Corners,
but it goes there. Good-by."

The girls went riding off on old Sam.
Down the long, pleasant road they went.

Right in the middle of the cool woods,
old Sam stopped to rest.

"Oh, dear!" said Kitty. "If Sam goes
to sleep, we will never get to the store!"

After a while Sam walked slowly on.

By and by Kitty said, "Look, Nancy.
I see a red brick chimney sticking up
through the trees. Is that the store?"

"No," answered Nancy. "I think it's
a farmhouse."

Sleepy Sam walked on and on.

"There's a store," Kitty shouted.

"The red brick chimney we saw is
on that country store!"

"Yes," laughed Nancy. "And there
is Uncle Dick. What a joke on me!
I've been here often enough to know
where Uncle Dick's store is. But I've
always come a shorter way."

"Hello!" called Uncle Dick.

"Come in and have some ice cream."

Before the two girls could get down,
Sam did a queer thing. He turned quickly
and started back the way he had come.

Sam opened his mouth and lifted his head.

"Hee-ee!" he said and started galloping.

Bumpety, bumpety, bump went the girls. Bumpety, bumpety, bumpety, bump!

Before they knew it, they were home.

When Father saw them, he said, "My! I thought you would stay longer!"

"Oh!" said Nancy. "Sam played a joke on us. He turned around and came home. He isn't as slow as you thought."

"No," laughed Father. "Sam goes fast when he is coming home to rest."

Stop and Go

Trot, trot, trot, trot came a pony
to Oak Tree Farm one summer day.

Behind the pony rolled a red cart.

In the cart sat David Wood.

"Oh, David," shouted Jack, "you have
a new cart! You have a fine new cart
for Trot!"

When Jack quit shouting, David said,
"This isn't a new cart. My grandfather
had this cart when he was a boy.

But it has a new coat of red paint."

"I want to ride," cried Jack.

"Climb in," said David. "I'll take all of you to Four Corners for ice cream."

Jack ran to ask Father if they could go. Then the children climbed into the cart.

"Let's go, Trot!" they shouted.

But Trot did not go. He stood still in the middle of the driveway.

The sun got hotter and hotter.

David clucked to the little pony, but nothing happened. Trot just stood still.

David clucked again and shook the lines, but Trot did not move.

"This is queer," said David. "Trot has never stopped like this before."

Just then Mr. Winters came along.

He said, "I've been watching Trot from the barn. I think he's listening for the right word to make him go. Let me say my magic word."

Mr. Winters put his mouth near
Trot's ear and whispered into it.

The pony jumped! Then away he went!

"I wonder what Father whispered,"
said Tom. "I guess it was a magic word
because it made Trot start so quickly."

Jack said, "I'm glad that Father knew
a magic word. But does Trot know the way
to the store? This isn't the way to go!"

"Yes, it is, Jack," said Nancy. "But it
isn't the shortest way to Four Corners.
We always go a shorter way in the car.

This old sand road isn't the shortest way,
but it's the best way to go in the cart."

Soon the children were in the store
eating the ice cream David had paid for.

They told Uncle Dick how Trot
stood still and would not go.

"Father said a magic word to Trot and
made him go," Tom said. "We should
know what it is so we can use it."

"H-m-m!" said Uncle Dick. "I know
a word that seems to be a magic word.

People often do what you ask when
you use it. Maybe a pony would, too.
The word starts with the letters PL."

Tom cried, "I know what the word is.
I'll try it if Trot stops again."

Tom wanted to drive on the way home.
So David let him hold the lines.

At first Trot went very quickly down
the cool country road. Soon he began
to trot a little slower.

Suddenly he stopped and stood still
in the middle of the sandy road.

David took hold of the lines and
shook them. But Trot did not move.
He seemed like a pony made of wood.

"Get up, wooden pony!" cried David.

Jack laughed and shouted, "Get up,
wooden pony! Lift your wooden legs!"

Quickly Tom jumped out of the cart.

He put his mouth near Trot's ear and whispered into it.

Trot started with a quick jump, but Tom got into the cart as it went past.

Trot did not seem like a wooden pony any longer. He went galloping home.

When Tom saw his father, he shouted, "I know what your magic word is!

The pony stopped again, and I used the magic word. I whispered PLEASE in Trot's ear, and away he went.

He went so fast that the long old road seemed like the shortest way home."

Father laughed and said, "PLEASE is a magic word. But I'll tell you a joke about that whisper in Trot's ear.

When you whispered in his ear, you blew in it. And when you blow in a pony's ear, he just can't stand still."

The Kitten That Worked

Play and eat! Wash and sleep!
That is what Penny did all day long.
Penny was Ann Wells' yellow kitten.
Ann was always good to her pet.

She gave Penny fish and cream and
other things that a kitten likes to eat.

Ann saved her pennies and bought
many toys for the kitten to play with.
Often she played games with Penny.

One Friday after breakfast Ann
was watching Penny wash her face.

"Go on. Wash your face!" said Ann.
"That is just what you should be doing.

Wash your face clean. You must wash
your coat, too, because Mr. Fall is going
to take your picture."

"Mew! Mew!" said Penny as if she
were asking, "What is a picture?"

Ann went on talking.

"Our family is going on a long trip,"
she said. "But we can't take you along.

I'll miss you, but Mother says that I
may take your picture with me.

Maybe it will make the trip seem
a little shorter."

When the kitten was through washing
her face, Ann picked her up.

"Good-by, Mother," she called as she
hurried off to Mr. Fall's.

Ann stopped in Mr. Fall's doorway.
She saw that Mr. Fall was not ready to
take a picture of Penny. He was trying
to take a picture of Mrs. Day's baby.

Mr. Fall and the baby's mother were
trying to get the baby to stop crying.

The mother waved her handkerchief
above her head and said, "Smile, Jill!"

Mr. Fall was holding a wooden clown.

"This clown should make Jill smile,"
he said. "When her mouth turns up
in a big smile, I'll take her picture."

But Jill went on making a noise. She
cried and cried and cried.

"Mew! Mew! Mew!" said Penny.

Suddenly she jumped out of Ann's arms right into the middle of the room.

Then she began to jump at the clown, which Mr. Fall was still holding.

All at once Jill stopped crying, and the corners of her mouth turned up.

"Kitty, kitty! Kitty, kitty, kitty!" she called in her soft baby voice.

Mr. Fall took a picture of little Jill with her face all smiles. Then he lifted her down to play with Penny.

"I wish I had a kitten or a cat," he said, "It would make babies smile when I take their pictures."

"Oh," cried Ann, "will you keep Penny while I'm away? I'll pay for her food. I've saved lots of pennies and dimes."

Mr. Fall laughed and said, "I'll keep Penny without any pay. She can work for her living by making babies smile."

"How funny!" laughed Ann. "A kitten can work for her living while she plays!"

Mr. Fall took a picture of Penny playing with the toy clown. Ann took Penny's picture with her on the trip.

She showed the picture and told everyone about Penny and the babies.

So Ann's long, long trip seemed like the shortest trip she had ever had.

Almost before she knew it, the trip was over. When she went to get Penny, she said, "Oh, Mr. Fall! Everyone liked Penny's picture. Everyone wanted to see the kitten that worked for her living."

Home Wanted!

"Well!" thought Nancy Winters as she peeped into the letter box by the road.

"Mr. Banks didn't have any letters or papers for us. So he played a joke on us today.

He put a pile of sticks in the middle of the letter box."

Quickly Nancy knocked the sticks out of the box and ran back to the house.

"Mother! Oh, Mother!" Nancy called in a laughing voice. "Mr. Banks played a joke on us today. He put sticks in the letter box."

"Was the box open?" asked Mother.

"Yes. Just a wee crack," said Nancy.

"Maybe Mrs. Wren played the joke," said Mother. "A wee crack would be big enough for her to get in.

The letter box would be a good home for her. No rain could get in. No cats could get in to eat her babies."

"Oh!" said Nancy. "I'm sorry I knocked the sticks out. I know that Mrs. Wren worked a long time to bring them."

"Yes," Mother said. "But Mr. Banks has to use the box to hold our letters.

We can put an old can on the fence for a nest. Mrs. Wren should like it almost as well as the letter box."

"Oh, my!" said Nancy the next day.
"Here are more sticks in the letter box."

As Nancy knocked all the sticks out,
two screaming wrens flew above the box.

"K-e-e! K-e-e! K-e-e!" they screamed.

Nancy said, "Quit screaming and
carry your sticks to that old can.

You should take the shorter sticks
because the longer ones won't go in."

Still the wrens flew above the box.
They screamed and screamed at Nancy.

She said to the wrens, "I'm sorry that
you can't hide your nest in the box.
I'm afraid you will go away if you can't."

Then Nancy sat down to think about what she could do.

"I wish the wrens could use the box," she said to herself. "But where would Mr. Banks put our letters and papers?"

Then she cried, "I know! I'll wait for Mr. Banks every day. He won't have to put letters in the box. And the wrens can make a nest for their babies in it."

The next day Nancy was sitting alone by the road waiting for Mr. Banks.

He met her there day after day.

At last he said, "Playing should be more fun than waiting for me every day."

Nancy just smiled at Mr. Banks.

She wanted to surprise him. So she did not tell him why she sat there alone, waiting for the letters every day.

She did not tell him that some babies would soon be living in the letter box.

Each day Nancy watched the wrens
bring more sticks to the box. Then they
began carrying in grass and straws.

They flew off to the field and back to
the box, carrying straws. Back and forth.
Back and forth. Back and forth.

"Hurry!" said Nancy. "You must
carry lots of straws."

At last the nest was ready.

In a week there were six eggs in it.

Then Mrs. Wren sat on the eggs.

Mr. Wren flew back and forth,
carrying bugs for her to eat.

One day Nancy heard bird voices
inside the letter box. Mrs. Wren's eggs
had cracked open. Her babies were out!

How excited Nancy was! How she
wished Mr. Banks would hurry!

When he came, he said, "I'm glad
you're here today. Your box won't hold
all the things I have for your family."

"No!" said Nancy. "It won't hold
any of them. Peep through the crack
and see why."

When Mr. Banks opened the box,
he said, "It's full all right!"

And it was. It was full
of Mrs. Wren's babies.

How Skip Found Joe

Skip was Joe Day's dog.

Joe often said to his brother John, "Skip is the best dog on Oak Street.

He has the shortest legs I ever saw on any dog. But he can run fast.

He is smart, too. He almost talks."

When Joe said that, Skip would wag his tail and bark, "Bow-wow."

Skip's bow-wow seemed to be saying, "Yes, I am smart!"

One Saturday Skip went with Joe and
his brother to visit Tom at the farm.

The three boys played games and
went sliding down the hay in the barn.

Skip went off alone to run after rabbits.
He was not back at five o'clock, and
Joe had to go home without him.

After a long while Skip got tired
of trying to catch a rabbit. He came
back to the barn, looking for Joe.

Joe was gone!

Skip sniffed the cracks in the floor.
He barked at the hay above his head.
He ran out of the barn, barking as loud
as he could. But he could not find Joe.

Skip was very tired. He ran slower
and slower and slower. His barks were
getting shorter and shorter and shorter.

He wanted his supper. But he was not
going home to supper alone.

"Skip, come to supper," Tom called from the house.

The puppy almost knocked Tom over as he ran in through the kitchen door.

But Skip did not eat supper. He ran from the kitchen to the living room, sniffing at all the chairs. One chair smelled like Joe, but Joe was not on it.

Back and forth ran the puppy.

At last Tom pointed out the door.

"Go home, Skip! Go home!" he said.

But Skip would not leave.

"Oh, Skip!" said Tom. "You are not as smart as Joe thinks you are. He said you would go home when I told you to."

Skip listened to Tom with a queer look
in his eyes. He always went home
when Joe said, "Home, Skip."

But Joe was not here!

Just then Tom ran out of the kitchen
to answer the telephone.

Skip followed Tom out of the kitchen.
He followed him into the living room.
He sat by the chair while Tom talked.

Suddenly Skip lifted his ears.

Joe's voice was coming through
the telephone above Skip's head. Skip
was so excited that his tail went tap, tap
on the floor. Tap, tap, tap!

"Bow-wow! Bow-wow!" he barked
as loud as he could. "Bow-wow!"

Then he jumped up on the chair.

Skip was excited and happy! He was
so excited that he almost knocked
the telephone out of Tom's hand.

"Listen, Skip," Tom said. "Joe wants to talk to you. Are you smart enough to know what he says on the telephone?"

Joe's voice called, "Home, Skip! Suppertime! Come home to supper."

How excited Skip was! He barked one loud bark into the telephone and jumped off the chair. Tom followed him to the kitchen door and opened it.

Soon Skip was at home on Oak Street.

"Smart dog!" Joe said.

"Smart dog!"

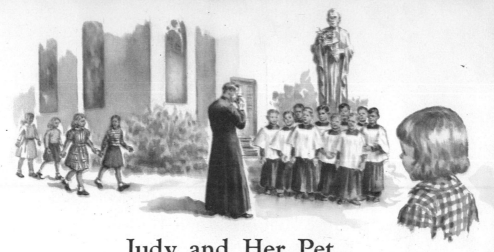

Judy and Her Pet

Judy stood alone watching Father White take pictures for the church paper.

First the priest took a picture of the boys who always helped him. They looked nice standing in front of Saint Joseph's statue.

The girls who sang in church each week followed the boys outside. They stood in front of the statue for their picture, too.

Judy thought, "I wish I could learn to do something nice for God.

But only boys may help the priest. And only big girls sing in church.

I'll have to wait until I grow up."

At home Judy took her pet mouse and sat down under a big maple tree. She began to sing to herself because it was so cool and pleasant under the maple tree.

"Thank You, oh, thank You, dear God," sang Judy. "Thank You for making this beautiful day."

"Squeak, squeak," sang the little mouse.

"Why, Squeaky," said Judy. "You can almost sing! Are you thanking God, too?"

When Judy had bought her pet, she had been told the mouse could learn to sing. At first Judy had tried and tried to get her pet to sing. But he would not learn. Now at last Squeaky was singing!

On Saturday morning Judy tried again to help Squeaky learn to sing.

At ten o'clock Ellen came by and said, "Don't forget that Sister wants some of us at school this morning."

"I wonder what for," said Judy.

"She didn't say," said Ellen. "We won't be there long. Come on."

Judy put the tiny mouse in her pocket and followed Ellen down the street.

At school Sister said, "Father White wants more girls to sing in church.

You girls are pretty small, but I think you can learn to do it. I want to hear you sing something now."

All the girls began to talk at once.

"My, how you chatter," said Sister. "You make more noise than the squirrel that chatters all day in the maple tree.

Let's save our voices for God."

The girls stopped chattering.

Sister told the girls what she wanted them to sing. Then she sat down and began to play.

As soon as Sister began to play, a tiny sound came from Judy's pocket.

"Oh, my!" thought Judy. "It's Squeaky. Poor dear! Why did I forget him!"

She put her hand in her pocket and tried to quiet the tiny animal.

But now Squeaky's singing was loud enough for Sister to hear.

"Oh, don't sing yet, girls," she said. "I'll tell you when to start."

Sister began over again.

When she lifted her hand all the girls began to sing.

Squeaky began to sing, too.

Poor Judy! Sister stopped playing and looked at her.

"Try to sing with the others, dear,"
Sister said to Judy in a friendly way.

"Your voice sounds too high. Now!
Let's try once more. Ready?"

Squeaky was ready. He sang as loud
as he could. Judy tried to sing loud, too,
so that Sister would not hear Squeaky.

At last Sister saw the tiny mouse.

Poor Judy was almost ready to cry.
She was afraid that Sister would never
let her sing in church now.

But Sister laughed and said, "Put your
little friend outside, Judy.

I think you can sing better by yourself."

At last the day came when Judy and
her friends were ready to sing in church.

Judy left home early so she would
have time to say some prayers.

As she ran across the churchyard
she saw Sister coming toward her.

Sister said, "There's no mouse hiding
in your pocket today, is there, Judy?"

"No, Sister. I'm alone today," said Judy.

She smiled because she was so happy.

She knew that she would soon be doing
something that she had wanted to do
for a long, long time.

New Storybook Friends

Billy Ground Hog Finds Spring

"Hello, Mr. Caw Crow. Is spring here yet?" asked Billy Ground Hog.

"Just this minute I waked up from my winter's sleep. I'll go right back to sleep if spring isn't here yet."

"Caw, caw, caw, caw!" said the crow from a branch of a maple tree. He laughed until he almost fell off the tiny branch.

"What's so funny about my asking if spring is here?" asked Billy. But the crow just sat on his branch and laughed.

"Oh, pooh, Mr. Crow!" Billy said. "I'll ask someone who isn't so silly."

Soon Billy met some ducks and geese.

"Hello!" he called in a friendly voice.
"Has spring come yet?"

"Quack, quack, quack!" said the ducks.

"Honk, honk!" said the geese.

They all began to laugh and chatter.
At last one old gray goose said,
"Oh, Billy! You can answer that!"

"Yes," quacked a duck, hiding a smile.
"You can answer that yourself."

"Pooh!" said Billy as he walked away.
"Pooh! I don't care what ducks and
geese say. Ducks and geese are silly!"

Soon Billy met Grandfather Turtle.

Billy thought that the turtle would not
laugh at him. So he said, "Is spring
here yet, Grandfather Turtle?"

Hiding a smile, Grandfather Turtle
answered, "If you don't know, who does?"
Then the turtle laughed right out loud.

Billy walked away from the turtle.
He wondered why the crow, the geese,
the ducks, and the turtle laughed at him.

Just then he heard some loud chattering.
It was two bluejays on a tiny branch.

"Jay! Jay! Jay!" they chattered.

Tap, tap, tap went some woodpeckers.

Billy said, "I'll ask those bluejays
and woodpeckers if spring is here yet."

When Billy asked the bluejays and
woodpeckers, they laughed at him, too.

"Of all things!" said one woodpecker.

Another woodpecker said, "Why would
a ground hog ask if spring has come?"

Poor Billy walked on toward home.

"Pooh, pooh!" he said.

"Pooh, pooh to everyone! I won't talk to any more silly animals.

I should run into my warm home and go back to sleep. But I'm not sleepy."

Suddenly he heard voices above him.

"Hello, young Billy Ground Hog," called Mr. Bluebird in a friendly voice. "I'm very glad to see you out today."

"Why?" asked the little ground hog. "Why are you so glad to see me?"

"I was afraid we hadn't been wise," said Mr. Bluebird. "I was afraid we had come back to our maple tree too early.

But here you are! So spring is here. Ground hogs don't wake up and leave their warm homes until spring comes."

Now Billy Ground Hog knew why he was not sleepy. He knew why everyone had laughed at him. Now the sound of Billy's laughing filled the woods.

At last Billy knew that he, himself, was one of the signs of spring.

Mrs. Goose Forgets

Early one Friday silly Mrs. Goose
came knocking on the schoolhouse door.

She came knock, knock, knocking
with one end of her big blue umbrella.

Miss Gray Squirrel, the teacher, heard
the sound and came to open the door.

"Come in, Mrs. Goose," she said.
"Come in and make yourself at home."

Miss Squirrel pointed to a chair, but
Mrs. Goose was too excited to sit down.

She waddled about as she chattered,
"I just came to ask—. I came to ask—.
Now what was it I came to ask?"

Mrs. Goose looked down at the string
on her neck and said, "Oh, dear me!
I forgot what I wanted to ask.

I tied this string on my neck so that I
wouldn't forget. But I forgot anyway.

I know it was about something that
young animal children learn at school."

The friendly teacher said, "They learn
to read storybooks. Did you want to ask
about reading a storybook?"

"No, no, no!" chattered Mrs. Goose,
still looking at the string on her neck.
"I can read as well as you can yourself.

And I can count. Just hear me count.
One, three, six, four, two, five, ten!"

When Mrs. Goose was through counting, she said, "I can sing, too!"

Hiding a smile, the friendly teacher said, "Can you sing as well as you can count?"

"Just hear me sing," said Mrs. Goose.

Her singing was very bad. It was so bad that all the animal children were hiding smiles, too.

Suddenly Mrs. Goose stopped singing.

"Oh, I forgot!" she cried. "I forgot that I left apples boiling on the fire.

If those apples burn, I can't fill cans with apple butter for the winter."

Mrs. Goose waddled out the door, carrying her big blue umbrella.

She got home before the apples burned and made her apple butter.

Again Mrs. Goose looked at the string on her neck. She put on her warm coat. She picked up her hat and umbrella.

Then she waddled back to school.

"What are all the young animals learning now?" she asked.

Miss Squirrel said, "I'm teaching them to paint roses. Would you like for me to teach you how to paint a rose?"

"You don't have to teach me to paint any roses," said Mrs. Goose. "Just see for yourself what a fine rose I can paint."

Splash, splash, splash went the paint!

Poor Mrs. Goose painted a rose that looked like a cabbage on a branch.

Soon the animal children began to write.

"Oh!" said Mrs. Goose. "I almost forgot that I must write something.

I always put names on the cans I fill with food for winter. I must hurry home and write the words APPLE BUTTER."

Mrs. Goose waddled toward the door. Then she waddled right back again.

"Now I know why I tied this string on my neck!" she cried. "I want to ask how to write the word BUTTER. I want to know how many T's are in it."

All at once she began to squawk and wave her umbrella in the teacher's face.

"What is the matter with this school?" she squawked as she waved her umbrella.

"You teach all the children to read and write. But you never teach them to write the word BUTTER. How am I to know how many T's are in it?"

"Oh," said the teacher, "my children learned to write that word last winter."

"Two T's!" shouted all the children, hiding their smiles.

Then Mrs. Goose quit squawking. She became as nice as she could be.

"Thank you," she said with a smile. "How wise and kind you are! I'm sorry I squawked those loud squawks at you."

Then she waddled out the door, saying to herself, "Two T's! Two T's!"

She hurried home and began to write APPLE BUTTER as fast as she could.

This time Mrs. Goose did not forget.

Everything There Is

Tim was a little goat that had never been outside his pen in the barnyard.

The yellow sun was warm and pleasant in his pen. Leaves were always blowing in the wind. Woodpeckers drummed on the barn. Often Mrs. Duck and her babies went quacking across the barnyard.

Tim liked to see those pretty things and to hear all those pleasant sounds.

Tim liked to sniff good smells.

He liked to taste things, too. But all he had ever tasted was milk, green grass, and hay that Johnny gave him.

From *Hoppity*, by Miriam Mason.
Copyright, 1947,
by the Macmillan Company and used with their permission.

One day Farmer Zeke let young Tim
out of his pen to play with Johnny.

They played until they were hungry.
Then Johnny went in to eat lunch, and
Tim began to taste things.

He tasted some weeds by the fence.
But he ate only a few of those because
he soon found a way into the garden.

"M-m!" he said as he tasted a head
of cabbage and a few ears of green corn.
"I want to taste everything there is!"

Just then Farmer Zeke came running
to take young Tim back to his pen.

The next day the farmer said to Tim,
"You may play with Johnny again today.
But if you are wise, you won't eat
anything that you shouldn't."

The gray goat was no longer listening.
"New things to taste!" he thought.

Tim soon saw a few bright red flowers
in the back yard. He filled his mouth
with flowers, and they tasted very good.

Then above his head he saw something.
It was the same red color as the flowers.

As Tim tasted it, Mrs. Zeke screamed,
"You bad goat! Let my coat alone!"

Then she put Tim back in his pen.
For two days he tasted nothing new.

On the third day Farmer Zeke said,
"Perhaps you will be good now, Tim."

Farmer Zeke let the goat out of his pen
and went to the house to eat breakfast.

Tim followed the farmer. He saw him
sit down before a big pile of pancakes.

Suddenly Tim heard Mrs. Zeke shout,
"Oh, dear! The cows are in the road!"

Out toward the road ran the family, and
into the kitchen ran the little gray goat.

He sniffed the good pancake smell.

"I must taste a few of those things
that smell so good," he said.

When the family came back, Tim was
eating the last pancake.

After that Tim was shut in his pen for a week. When at last the farmer let him out of his pen, Tim did not taste a thing in the yard.

He stood in the warm sunlight and saw flowers blowing in the wind. He listened to the chattering of voices in the house.

Tim peeped in an open window.

He did not see people, but he did see a bed with hats on it. Beautiful hats! Hats with feathers! Hats with flowers!

"I must taste those," he thought.

In through the window he went, and up in the middle of the bed he hopped.

As Tim tasted the last hat, a honeybee came buzzing into the bedroom.

"Oh, good! Here's something that I've never tasted before," Tim thought.

He opened his mouth, and in went the honeybee.

The bee tasted hot! Burning hot!
The goat's mouth became very hot!
Tim danced and jumped. He hopped
up and down in the middle of the bed.

Then he opened his mouth and let out
a squeaky cry. He let the bee out, too.

Right then young Tim said to himself,
"I'll never taste anything new again!"

And he never, never did.

The Old Woman's New Hat

Old Mrs. Wise always was smiling and never was sad. She had a brick house and lots of flowers. She had a straw hat with a bright red feather on it.

Every time she went out, she put on the hat and tied it at her neck. But one day she could not find the hat.

The old woman looked in every box and under the chairs and under the bed.

Her hat with the red feather was lost!

Right then and there poor Mrs. Wise quit smiling and became very sad.

Mrs. Wise was sad for only a while.
Soon she was smiling the same as before.

"It's queer that I lost my hat," she said.
"But I won't be sad any longer.

I can get a new hat with a feather.
Perhaps a hat with a yellow feather
would look better than the one I lost.

Miss Ellen made my old hat. She can
make me a new one by tonight.

I'll stop and see Miss Ellen on my way
to the store. But I can't go to see her
without taking some flowers."

Mrs. Wise found a large flower basket.
Out into the bright sunlight she went
to fill the basket with flowers.

"I'll cut some of every kind," she said.
"I'll have only a few of the same color."

At last the flower basket was filled.

Taking it with her, Mrs. Wise walked
out toward Christmas Tree Road.

A squeaky old farm wagon came along while Mrs. Wise was shutting her gate.

Her neighbor, Mr. Bright, was taking chickens and pigs to town in his wagon.

When the gate banged shut, the horse jumped at the noise. The wagon turned over right in Christmas Tree Road.

Mrs. Wise screamed. Pigs grunted and squealed. Chickens squawked.

One squealing pig became so excited that it ran down the middle of the road.

Mr. Bright became so excited that he danced around and shouted, "Stop! Stop! All of you stop!"

The runaway pig went on running away.

The pig in the wagon went on grunting and squealing.

The chickens went right on squawking.

All that loud squawking and squealing excited Mrs. Wise. Suddenly she turned her flower basket over her head and ran to catch the runaway pig.

The basket was upside down, and most of the flowers fell out. Only one pretty pink rose stayed in the basket.

How queer Mrs. Wise looked with a pink rose peeping out over her ear!

But she did catch Mr. Bright's pig.

After taking the squealing pig back,
Mrs. Wise went on her way.

She was so proud of catching the pig
that she forgot all about her basket.

It was still upside down on her head.

The pink rose was still over her ear
when she came to Miss Ellen's gate.

"Good afternoon!" called Miss Ellen.
"What a pretty new straw hat you have!

It's the only hat I've seen like that.
The pink rose looks nice by your ear.
You must be proud of that hat."

Mrs. Wise put her hand up to her head. There was her basket upside down! There was a pink rose over her ear!

"Well," she thought, "if an upside-down basket looks like a hat, perhaps it is!

If Miss Ellen thinks so, I'm sure that other people will think so, too.

If most people think it's a hat, I can think the same thing."

Mrs. Wise was smiling a proud smile as she walked toward the village.

"Well, well!" she said. "It just shows that we should always be smiling and happy and never be sad. Never be sad, no matter what happens!"

126

Little Mouse Dances

Once a merry little brown mouse lived in a tiny house on the very top of a hill.

This merry little mouse liked to dance.

Each morning she put a red paper rose over her ear. Then she began to skip and dance and sing.

She danced most of the day, singing,
"Why rub and scrub
All day in the house?
It's better to dance
Like Little Brown Mouse."

One afternoon Grandmother Mouse
came to visit. She looked all around.

Then her squeaky old voice said, "My!
What a lot of dust! You should rub
and scrub and clean your house."

"Not this afternoon!" said Little Mouse.

"I'll clean my house tonight. I want
to dance and sing this afternoon. I will
rub and scrub and clean tonight."

Out of the house and through the gate
she ran. Then down the grassy hill she
danced as if she had wings on her feet.

At the foot of the hill there was
a village. In the village there was
a store window with a red dress in it.

When the little mouse saw the dress,
she said, "I'm sure that pretty dress is
the same color as my rose. I'll buy it."

She bought the dress and put it on.

"I'm proud of this beautiful dress,"
she said. "I'll get it wet if I rub and
scrub in it. So tonight I won't rub and
scrub. I'll go dancing in the village."

Little Mouse danced most of the night
in her new red dress. She went dancing
around as if she had wings on her feet.

Grandmother Mouse came to visit
Little Mouse again the next afternoon.

Dust lay on the table. Dust lay
under the table. Dust lay on the bed.
Dust lay under the bed. Dust lay
in all the cracks in the floor.

Grandmother said, "There is still dust
enough here to write your name in.
Perhaps you didn't have time to scrub."

"No, Grandmother," said Little Mouse.
"But I will be sure to scrub tonight.
I must go to the village store now."

Out the gate and down the hill she ran.
In the store window lay some shoes.

Little Mouse saw that the shoes were
the same color as her dress and her rose.
So she bought the beautiful red shoes.

She danced all afternoon and most of
the night in her new shoes. She danced
as if she had wings on her feet.

It was late when the mouse waked up.

She looked at her new dress.

She looked at her red shoes, which lay
on the table beside the bed.

Taking them from the table, she said,
"My! Such a lot of dust on these shoes.
I'm not proud of them. I can't go dancing
in these dusty shoes."

The little brown mouse began to rub
the shoes. Soon they were pretty again.

She blew the dust off the flower.

She blew on the dress and shook it.

How bright the dress and the rose
and the shoes looked then!

Suddenly the little mouse wanted
her tiny house to look the same way.

She began to rub and scrub and dust.

"I'll have plenty of time for dancing
when my work is done," she said. She flew
about as if she had wings on her feet.

When the work was done, she put on
her red dress, her flower, and her shoes.

Around the table she went dancing
as if she had wings on her feet.

She sang in her squeaky mouse voice,

"It's better to scrub
All day in the house
And dance at night
Like Little Brown Mouse."

The Little Engine

Once a farmer had some fine wheat.
He took his wheat to a station where
a long train of cars was standing.

He filled every car with wheat.

When that was done, the farmer said,
"Please carry my wheat to the city."

The cars all answered, "We will
be glad to carry your wheat for you.
But cars cannot move alone.

We must have an engine to pull us.
We must have a good engine to pull
such a long train to the city."

By the station was a big green engine.
It had only a few cars to pull.

The farmer thought, "That big engine
doesn't have to work hard. Perhaps it
will pull these cars of wheat."

So he called to the engine, "Will you
pull these cars to the city? My wheat
must get there before dark tonight."

The big green engine did not like
hard work. It liked only easy work.
Pulling cars to the city was not easy.

So the engine moved away
from the station, screaming,
"No-o-o! No-o-o! No-o-o!
That's too far for me to go."

The farmer went to a big red engine,
which stood nearby.

"You are such a large engine," he said.
"It will be easy for you to pull these
cars of wheat. I'm sure you will do it.

The wheat must go to the city
to be ground into flour.

The flour will be made into bread.

Then all the people will have plenty
of bread to eat this winter."

But the red engine fooled the farmer.
It backed away from the station, calling,
"Puff! Puff! I have worked enough!"

The poor man called to a third engine, which was standing near the station.

He said, "Please pull these cars filled with bags of wheat. The bags of wheat must get to the city tonight before dark.

The wheat will be ground into flour.

The flour will be made into bread.

Then all the people will have plenty of bread to eat this winter."

This engine was a lazy, lazy engine. It would do only very easy work.

It took one look at the long train of cars filled with bags of wheat.

Then the lazy engine's bell called out in a very lazy way, "Too long, too long!"

"Oh, dear!" said the sad, sad farmer. "Where is an engine that will take all my bags of wheat to be made into flour?"

Just then a squeaky little engine came bumping and banging along.

"I'll take the bags of wheat," it said. "I'll get the wheat to the city by six o'clock tonight. There's plenty of time."

"Fine!" said the farmer. "But it won't be easy for such a little engine to pull such a long train. Are you sure you can?"

The engine said, "I'm not lazy. I have done hard work for years and years."

So it pulled hard, and the cars filled with bags of wheat rolled slowly away.

Soon the engine came to a high hill. Up it started. It puffed and pulled and puffed harder and harder and harder.

As it pulled, it sang, "I think I can— I think I can—I think I can—"

Up, up, up, up went the little engine,
pulling harder and harder all the time.

It kept on singing, "I think I can—
I think I can—I think I can—"

Slowly and surely it pulled to the top.
Then it hurried down the other side.

Faster and faster it rolled down the hill.
Now it was singing, "I thought I could!
I thought I could! I thought I could!"

Soon the engine's work was done, and
all the bags of wheat were in the city.

Then the wheat was ground into flour.
The flour was made into bread, and
people had plenty of bread that winter.

The Most Beautiful Thing

One bright morning the Wind Fairy blew down from the hills. She danced in and out of the woods and across Smiling Pond. There she saw Grandfather Turtle.

"Good morning," Grandfather Turtle said. "Isn't this a beautiful morning?"

"It surely is," said the Wind Fairy. "There are other beautiful things, too. I think that I have just seen the most beautiful thing on earth."

"Where?" asked Grandfather Turtle.

"In Old Oak Woods," the Wind Fairy answered. Then she went dancing away.

Adapted from *Mother West Wind's Neighbors*,
by Thornton W. Burgess.
Copyright 1913, 1941 by Thornton W. Burgess.

Grandfather Turtle said to himself, "Now what can the Wind Fairy think is the most beautiful thing on earth?

Surely nothing can be more beautiful than the water flowers in my own pond.

Or the sun coming up in the morning.

Or the bright stars above me at night. Or those same stars smiling back at me from the deep waters of the pond.

But I can see those things right here.

If I weren't so slow, I would go and see what is in Old Oak Woods.

But that would be too hard for me."

Just then Grandfather Turtle saw Billy Ground Hog coming down the path to Smiling Pond.

"Billy," he called. "Billy Ground Hog! Come here."

Billy hurried on down the path to see what Grandfather Turtle wanted.

"The Wind Fairy just came dancing by to tell me something," said the old turtle.

"She said the most beautiful thing on earth is over in Old Oak Woods."

"Pooh!" said Billy Ground Hog. "Nothing beautiful in that old woods!"

"Oh, yes, there is!" said the turtle. "The Wind Fairy saw it. Really she did! But it can't be the sun or the stars or the pink water flowers. What can it be?"

"I don't know," said Billy. But he kept wondering what the Wind Fairy had seen.

"I'll go and find out." he said at last.

As Billy hurried down the path he saw Mrs. Robin sitting on a branch.

"Tweet, tweet, tweet," said Mrs. Robin. "Tweet, tweet! Where are you going?"

"To Old Oak Woods," said Billy. "To see the most beautiful thing on earth. The Wind Fairy just saw it. I know it's not pink water flowers or the sun or the stars. That's all I know about it."

"Tweet, tweet, tweet," said the robin. "I'll go, too." She hopped off the branch and flew along the path above Billy's head.

Soon Billy and the robin met a squirrel and a field mouse. Billy told them where he was going and they both went along.

Soon they all came to Old Oak Woods. Not a thing was changed in the woods. "Nothing beautiful here!" said Billy.

Just then he heard a little voice say, "What are you looking for?"

Billy's three friends kept quiet while
Billy pushed back some big weeds.

Then they saw Peter Rabbit in one
of his hiding places. Near him lay a pile
of nice leafy young plants. He was
feeding them to his baby brother.

Billy Ground Hog said, "We are looking
for the most beautiful thing on earth.
The Wind Fairy says it's in this woods.
Have you seen it, Peter Rabbit?"

Peter wiggled his pink ears and said,
"No, I haven't seen it."

"Come along then," said Mrs. Robin.

Peter wanted to go with the others,
but the wee bunny was still hungry.

Peter said, "I'll meet you after a while."
Then he kept on feeding the bunny until
the last leafy young plant was gone.

Only then did Peter go to meet the others.

The five friends looked everywhere.

They kept on looking until they were tired.

But they could find nothing as beautiful
as the sun or the stars or the flowers
in Smiling Pond.

At last they gave up.

Billy went down the path to Smiling Pond.

He saw Grandfather Turtle and said, "We can't find the most beautiful thing on earth. We looked all through the woods. But nothing is changed there.

All we saw was Peter Rabbit feeding nice leafy plants to his baby brother."

Grandfather Turtle thought a minute. He knew it was not very easy to find nice leafy young plants.

He knew Peter must have wanted to stop at once and go with his friends.

"H-m-m," said the wise old turtle. "The Wind Fairy was surely right. She did see the most beautiful thing on earth. You saw it, too, but you didn't know it.

You saw it when you saw Peter Rabbit feeding all those nice leafy young plants to his little baby brother.

It's something we call 'love.'"

Second Helpings

Every woman in Maple Village baked good things to eat. But the best things in Maple Village were baked by Mrs. Smart.

Her rolls were as light as feathers. Sometimes they were so light that they blew away if they were not eaten at once.

So she tied strings on them, and they flew around her kitchen like balloons.

Mrs. Smart made wonderful cakes, too. She was always making a new kind.

One afternoon she took butter, eggs, flour, milk, and honey. She cut up a few apples, cracked a few nuts, and made a really new kind of cake.

The new cake smelled so good that
Mrs. Smart telephoned some neighbors.

"Meet me for supper tonight in the park,"
she said. "Meet me by the boat pond."

"A party!" they cried. "We will meet
you by the boat pond at six o'clock."

So at sundown all the neighbors met
near the Maple Village boat pond.

Mr. and Mrs. Small had a basket
filled with food and cold drinks.

Mr. Bell said, "I didn't bring things
to eat or drink. I have a red balloon and
a blue balloon for May and Tommy Small."

Mr. Gay did not say what he had.

Mrs. Small began taking food and cold drinks from her large basket.

She put chicken, bread and butter, cold milk, and cookies on the table.

Everyone began eating and drinking.

Soon Mrs. Smart asked, "Is everyone ready for my apple-and-nut cake?"

"Oh, dear! Not I," said Mr. Bell. "I've eaten too much now."

"So have I," Mr. Small said. "I have eaten too much, and I've been drinking too much milk. I really can't eat cake."

"Now!" said Mr. Gay. "We can use what I brought to this party. I brought my fiddle. You can surely eat cake if you do a little dancing first.

I'll play my fiddle while you dance.

It's time I did something to earn my dinner. I'll earn it with my fiddle."

Soon merry sounds filled the park.

Mrs. Small picked up a pan and used it for a drum. She drummed and drummed.

Mr. Gay fiddled and fiddled and fiddled. The other two men went dancing around the table with Tommy and his sister.

At last Mrs. Smart said, "You have fiddled and drummed enough! So stop dancing and eat some apple-and-nut cake. Mr. Gay has earned his cake by this time."

So she cut some cake for each neighbor at the party. But she gave Mr. Gay the biggest helping because he had earned it.

After the people had eaten their cake,
they washed their hands in the pond.

As they came back from the boat pond,
Mr. Bell said, "That was the best cake
I've ever eaten. What kind was it?"

"Upside-down cake," said Mrs. Smart.
"Why are you walking on your hands?"

Mr. Bell asked in surprise, "Me?
Walking on my hands? So I am!"

"So are the others!" cried Mrs. Smart.
"Their feet almost touch the branches
of the maple trees. Tell me why you are
all walking on your hands."

No one could answer Mrs. Smart.

Suddenly she cried, "Perhaps my cake did it! All of you ate upside-down cake. All of you are walking on your hands.

I'm the only one on my feet. I haven't eaten any cake. I haven't had time."

"The cake!" shouted Mr. Gay.

"The cake is surely what did it!

Now we need to get changed about. How shall we get right side up?"

"I know!" said Mrs. Smart. "Each of you must eat another helping of cake.

You will turn upside down again, but you will really be right side up!"

She began to feed cake to everyone. One by one they turned right side up.

"I'm surely glad I had plenty of cake," Mrs. Smart said. "The next time I have upside-down cake, I'll see that everyone gets two helpings at once."

Mr. Hurry Changes Things

Mr. Hurry lived on a farm.

Behind his barn was a very tall hill.
Behind the very tall hill was a forest
of maple trees. In the maple forest
was his henhouse full of hens.

Each day Mr. Hurry went to the forest,
taking food to his hens and water
for them to drink.

He had to go up the tall hill, down
the tall hill, and into the maple forest.

One day Mr. Hurry said, "Fiddlesticks!
This trip really takes too long. I shall
change things. I'll move this tall hill."

Away he hurried to Neighbor Black's.

"Mr. Black!" he said. "I need to move the tall hill by my maple forest. May I use your digging machine to move it?"

"You surely may," said Mr. Black. "I earn my living by digging ponds with my machine. Moving a tall hill will be easy work for my digging machine."

Before he lent the machine to Mr. Hurry, Mr. Black told him how to start it.

"Look!" he said. "Touch this and put your foot on that."

"I see," said Mr. Hurry.

"Now!" said Mr. Black. "I shall teach you how to drive this machine. And I shall teach you to work the big shovel."

"Not yet," said Mr. Hurry. "Just let me learn to start the engine first."

The two men changed places.

Mr. Hurry touched this and then he touched that. And the engine started!

Then he touched something else.

Away toward Mr. Jolly's garden went the machine and Mr. Hurry.

"It's moving!" he called to Mr. Black. "How do I stop it? Run fast and tell me!"

Mr. Black ran, but he did not catch up.

"Fiddlesticks!" said Mr. Hurry. "I can find the thing that stops this machine."

He saw something that looked like a long stick, so he gave it a hard pull.

The big shovel dropped down and began to dig up the earth in Mr. Jolly's garden.

"Help! It's digging!" cried Mr. Hurry. "Some hives are right in our path!"

Quickly he pushed the stick. Up came the shovel, and the beehives were in it. Off went the machine, carrying the hives.

"Buzz, buzz, buzz." Angry bees flew out of their hives, stinging and buzzing.

"Bring back my bees!" called Mr. Jolly. But the machine was moving on toward Mrs. Blue's apple tree. Her cow, Dolly, was standing under its leafy branches.

Mr. Hurry became excited and pulled the stick again. Down fell the hives, and the shovel began digging up the earth.

Mr. Hurry gave the stick a quick push.
Up came Dolly, swishing through
the leafy branches of the apple tree.

Dolly's angry moo scared Mrs. Blue,
who had gone to hoe her cabbage plants.

Mrs. Blue quit hoeing. She screamed
in an angry voice, "Put Dolly down!"

The machine was moving into the road,
carrying Dolly and a few green branches.

After it ran a long parade of neighbors.

Suddenly the machine ran off the road
toward Mrs. Short's henhouse.

Mr. Hurry pulled and pushed the stick. Down fell Dolly. Up came the henhouse.

The machine kept on rolling down the road, carrying the henhouse along.

Bumpety-bang! Bumpety-bang!

Bumpety, bumpety, bumpety, bang!

Before Mr. Hurry knew it, the machine was moving into his own barnyard.

There Mrs. Short's henhouse fell off.

On went the machine, digging a path across fields of hay and corn and wheat.

The machine stopped at Mr. Black's, and up ran the parade of angry people.

"At last!" shouted tired Mr. Hurry. "I stopped this thing at last!"

"You didn't stop it," said Mr. Black in an angry voice. "It stopped because there is nothing left to make it go."

"Fiddlesticks!" said Mr. Hurry.

"I shall fill it and make it go again. I'll move everything back where it was."

"I'm tired of honey," said Mr. Jolly. "Mrs. Blue may keep my beehives."

"If I keep the hives, Mrs. Short may have Dolly," cried Mrs. Blue. "I really like honey better than milk. And bees won't eat apples and branches off my tree."

"Oh!" said Mrs. Short. "Dolly can eat grass in my yard. I won't have to cut it. I don't have hens. So I really don't need a henhouse. Mr. Hurry may have it."

"Thanks!" said Mr. Hurry. "I won't need to move my tall hill after all."

Friends at Work

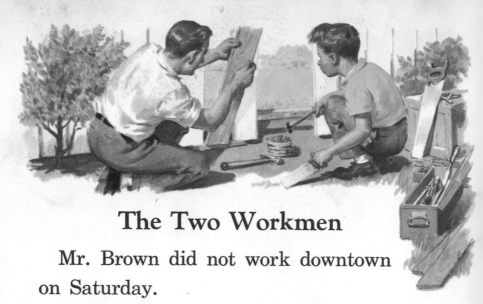

The Two Workmen

Mr. Brown did not work downtown on Saturday.

That was when he fixed things around the house at 110 Oak Street.

On sunny Saturdays he liked to work outside. He cut and raked the grass. He put new boards in the fence. He fixed the back gate so it would open and shut.

On rainy Saturdays he always found something else to fix inside the house.

Jay liked to help his father fix things.

Jay always tried to use his toy saw and toy hammer when he helped. But there was never much he could do with them.

One bright Saturday the two workmen were building new back steps.

Jay had his toy hammer and his saw. They were not much help, but Jay was.

He helped hold the heavy boards while his father sawed them. He handed Father his big heavy hammer when he needed it.

"You are good help, Jay," said Father.

"Someday you will be a fine workman like Saint Joseph was. When you are ten years old, you may have a real hammer and a saw of your own."

"I won't be ten for two years!" said Jay.

Father laughed. "It may take that long to save the money to buy them," he said.

"If I save for two whole years, I can buy lots of hammers," Jay said.

That night Jay counted the pennies and dimes in his bank. Each week after that he saved a few more dimes or pennies.

One day just before noon Jay ran in
to ask how soon lunch would be ready.

Jay knew that his mother was washing.
He ran through the living room and
down the kitchen stairs.

From the foot of the stairs Jay saw
some water in the middle of the floor.

Right in the middle of the water
stood Mother.

"I can't turn this water off," she said.
"I telephoned some men to come and fix
the water tap. But the men can't come
before four o'clock. What else can we do?"

162

"I know," said Jay. "We must shut the water off from the whole house.

I've often seen Father do that, and I know what he uses to do it."

Off ran Jay to get the thing he needed. It was heavy, but Jay brought it quickly.

"Look," he said, pointing above his head. "That's where we shut off the water."

"You can't reach that," said Mother. "You aren't tall enough. Here is a chair for you to stand on."

"Now!" said Jay. "All I have to do is turn this round thing to the right."

The round thing was not easy to turn.
At first Jay could hardly turn it at all.

"There!" he said at last. "The water is shut off! No more can run from the tap."

That night at supper Jay's mother told his father what had happened.

"It surely was a good thing that Jay knew what to do," she said.

"Jay is a smart boy," said Father with a big smile on his face. "He is a good workman like Saint Joseph.

He has been helping me and learning to do things for a long time. He has been a helper long enough. It's time he had things of his own to work with."

The next afternoon Jay went downtown to meet his father.

They came home with all the things a young workman needs.

Jay was a real workman at last.

Molly Plays a Joke

Hammer and saw! Hammer and saw!
Joe and John Day were making a house
out of wooden boxes. The house was to be
a place to meet with their friends.

Molly Good had come over. She stood
on her roller skates, watching the boys.

"Do you need a helper?" she asked.

"What could you do?" asked the boys.

"I might help you hammer," she said.

"No," said Joe. "Girls can't hammer."

"I might help you saw," said Molly.

"No," said John. "Don't touch a thing.
We will be done by noon if we hurry."

Molly skated away on her roller skates.

Soon she thought of something else and came back, smiling.

"Aren't you going to have tables and chairs in your house?" she asked.

The boys did not answer Molly at all. They just began to hammer.

Molly kept right on smiling and talking.

The boys hammered louder and louder. So Molly chattered louder and louder.

"You really need tables and chairs," she shouted to the boys. "I might go to the store and get some wooden boxes to use for chairs. Shall I?"

Still the boys did not answer Molly. They just hammered louder than ever.

Molly's smiling face became sad.

"I'll just go to the grocery store and bring back boxes anyway," she thought. "The boys will need boxes for chairs."

Molly took off her roller skates and hurried home to get her wagon.

"The grocery man might give me some boards, too," she thought.

And he did. The grocery man piled two boxes and six boards on the wagon.

Taking all those heavy things home from the grocery store was hard work.

Two boards and a heavy wooden box went sliding off the wagon at once. Molly tried to pull with one hand and hold the boxes on the wagon with the other.

But the wagon would not roll straight. And it would hardly go through the gate into the Days' yard. Some of the boards fell off again.

"The grocery man gave me some boxes for chairs," Molly called from the gate.

"Oh!" cried Joe. "We don't need those wooden boxes. Mother will give us some old chairs and a table."

Then Molly thought of something else to do with the wooden boxes.

"You haven't any stairs yet," she said. "You might use these boxes for stairs."

Joe asked, "Why should we have stairs? A one story house doesn't need stairs."

"I know," said Molly. "But you might build a second story. You really need an upstairs and a downstairs."

"We haven't time to make an upstairs," said John. He reached for his hammer and started the loudest hammering of all.

Before very long Molly had thought of something else. As quick as could be, she ran to get something she needed.

When she came back, the boys were hammering their loudest. So Molly shouted her loudest.

"Here's paint for the floor," she called in her very loudest voice. "I have a can of dark blue paint and a can of yellow."

Joe said, "We really do need paint, but the cans are only part full! There's hardly enough of one color for the whole floor."

"No," said John. "Our floor can't be part blue and part yellow.

Come on, Joe. Let's get a cool drink before we do the rest of our work."

"I'll fool those boys," Molly thought.

"I'll put the two colors together and make green. I'll have plenty of green to paint the whole floor. And I'll do it."

Molly started her painting at the door.

Swish went the paint! Back and forth! Back and forth! Back and forth!

Soon part of the floor was painted.

The whole floor had to be painted before the boys got back. So Molly worked harder and harder on the last part.

At last she looked up. She could not move without stepping in wet paint!

Molly shouted her loudest for help, and soon the boys came running.

"I fooled myself," cried Molly. "I wanted to play a joke on you, but the joke is on me. I painted myself in."

"We will get you out," John said.

"We can't reach you from the door.
But we can cut a hole behind you."

John took his saw and began to cut
a hole for Molly to step through.

"I was a very bad helper," Molly said.
"I'm sorry you had to cut your house."

"We really needed a window for light,"
said John. "We just forgot to make one.

We never would have thought of it
if you hadn't painted yourself in.

Now the floor is painted!

The window is made!

And the house is done by noon!"

Aunt Susan's Clock

"Hello," said Nancy, reaching up to put her arms around Aunt Susan's neck. "Here we are for our Saturday visit."

"Hello, dears," said Aunt Susan.

"I was watching for you. I knew you would come as soon as you had eaten your breakfast.

I knew you would hurry straight down the path to my house for a visit.

So I said to myself, 'I must hurry and start my Saturday baking. Nancy and Jack and Tom will soon be here.'"

"M-m," said Tom as they all went
into Aunt Susan's brick house. "There is
a wonderful smell in this kitchen!

Let's play a guessing game and guess
what's baking in the oven. I say cookies!
And I can hardly wait to taste them."

"It might be nut cake," said Nancy.

Jack did not play the guessing game.
He knew that anything Aunt Susan
baked in her oven was sure to be good.

"You never will guess what is baking
in my oven today," said Aunt Susan.

"It's a surprise, and it isn't done yet.
It won't be done until noon."

Tom and Nancy looked quickly toward the kitchen clock above their heads.

Jack could not tell time. So he said, "Noon? Noon? How much longer is it until noon, Aunt Susan?"

"Not very long," she said. "Just watch the clock until the hands meet and point straight up. Then it will be noon."

All three children sat down to watch the clock. Jack wished he could peep into the oven, but he never took his eyes off the clock.

Minute after minute went by. The hands were moving slowly around the clock's face.

Jack was hungry. He could hardly wait
for the surprise. He was soon tired of
seeing the clock's hands moving so slowly.

"Hurry up! Lazy, lazy clock!" he said.
"You are as slow as a turtle!"

"Oh, Jack!" laughed Aunt Susan.

"A good clock never changes the way
it goes. It always goes the same way.
Not too fast! Not too slow!"

More minutes went slowly past.

At last Nancy hopped up and said,
"Aunt Susan needs a helper. I can't sit
and wait until the hands are straight up.

Please give me an apron, Aunt Susan.
I'll help wash the pots and pans."

"Fine!" said Aunt Susan. "I can use
a helper. Here's a pink apron for you."

"I'm a good strong helper," said Tom.
"I'll put the pots and pans away.
But I won't need an apron."

Tom and Nancy were good helpers.

Nancy put on the apron and helped with
the pots and pans. Tom carried them
across the kitchen and put them away.

Jack just kept his eyes on the clock.

"Will it ever be noon?" he wondered.

Part of the time Jack whispered,
"Straight up. Both hands must meet
and point straight up. When they meet,
the baking will be done."

At last the big hand gave a quick jump.

"Aunt Susan!" cried Jack. "It's noon!
Both of the clock's hands are pointing
straight up. Is the baking done?"

Aunt Susan said, "Yes. It's noon, and now the baking can come out of the oven."

She reached into the oven and got four big baked potatoes. She carried the baked potatoes to the table.

She reached into the oven again and took something else out.

"Apple pie!" cried Tom. "A pie for each one of us! What a wonderful surprise!"

Aunt Susan carried the four pies to a window and left them there to cool.

Soon lunch was ready. Nancy took off her apron and everybody sat down to eat.

When the pies were eaten, Tom said, "It surely didn't seem long until noon. Time really goes fast for busy people."

"Not always," said Jack. "Not when you're busy doing what I was. I was teaching myself to tell time."

How Not to Forget

Peter jumped out of bed quickly and put on his clothes. He had just remembered that he was going to Oak Tree Farm to stay the whole day with Tom Winters.

After breakfast Peter walked to the end of Oak Street and out toward the farm.

As he came near, he could see Tom doing the morning work. A puppy and three cats were following Tom as he carried feed to the chickens. The chickens were squawking and running to meet Tom.

Tom said, "Hello, you're just in time to help me feed the chickens. Next I must feed Puppy and the cats. Then I have an errand to do for Mother."

Peter said, "How can you remember so much? All I have to remember is to say my prayers. Sometimes I forget that."

Tom said, "Perhaps you could pin up a sign to make yourself remember."

"I did pin up a sign," said Peter. "It helps me at night. But in the morning I hop out of bed too fast to see it.

Maybe I might pin up a bigger sign."

Tom said, "I try to think of ways
to make myself remember things.

I never forget to feed the chickens.
They won't let me! So once, after I
forgot to water some little plants, I put
the water can on the bag of chicken feed.

When I went to get feed, I saw the can
and remembered to water the plants!"

"Oh, dear!" said Peter. "Everybody else
thinks of smart things, but I never do!"

Peter helped feed the puppy and cats.
Then Tom said, "Let's find Mother and get
the money for her errand. We must see
if the storekeeper sells heavy string.

We can ride Old Sam to the store."

The boys went past three beehives and found Mrs. Winters looking at some vines.

"Ready for my errand?" she asked, taking a nickel from her apron pocket.

"Please ask the storekeeper to sell you some string to hold up these heavy vines. Perhaps a nickel isn't enough. Let's see what else I can find in this pocket."

Mrs. Winters found a dime and two more nickels in her pocket.

"Two nickels are for candy," she said.

"Be sure the storekeeper sells you something strong enough to hold up these vines. And don't let the bees sting you when you go past the beehives!"

After the boys had done their errand, they played with the puppy for a while.

After dinner they went fishing.

When the day was over, Peter hurried home with two fish for his supper.

After supper, Peter was so tired that
he went straight upstairs to bed.

He was about to jump into bed when he
saw the sign, so he said his prayers.

Then he said, "Dear Jesus, please
don't let me forget in the morning."

All of a sudden Peter thought
of something. He pushed his shoes
under the bed as far as he could reach.

"There!" he said. "In the morning
I'll have to get down on my knees to reach
my shoes. While I'm on my knees,
I'll remember to say my prayers!"

PRAYERS

182

The Birthday Present

It was a warm, lazy day, just right
for Tom to go riding on Sleepy Sam.

They made a detour so the old horse
could get a cool drink from Deep Pond.

While Sam was drinking, Tom listened
to the tweet, tweet of birds. In Deep Pond
he saw an old turtle and two turtle babies.

In a leafy tree he saw a woodpecker
flying from branch to branch to get bugs.

Tom pushed his knees into Sam's back
and the old horse walked on. The day
became hotter and hotter. At the road,
Sam stopped again to rest and cool off.

Tom listened to the soft, lazy sounds.
Leafy branches and vines along the fence
were blowing in the wind.

Bees from his father's hives buzzed
in and out of the vines.

All of a sudden Tom heard loud noises.
Honk! Cluck, cluck! Squawk! Bang!
Then he heard a man's angry cries.
Tom used his knees to make Sam trot
toward the sounds.

A grocery truck had run off the road.
The truck was the small grocery truck
that Uncle Dick Gray carried groceries in.
The storekeeper stood beside his truck.
"You silly clucking hens!" he shouted.
"Why don't you stay in your pen?"

"What happened?" called Tom.

"Oh," said his uncle, "I ran off the road to keep from hurting those hens.

My truck didn't touch them. But here I am while everybody waits for things.

Mrs. Wood needs clothespins and a new clothesline to pin her washing to.

Your Aunt Susan is waiting for butter, flour, cabbage, and other groceries.

But I can't get my truck out of here."

Tom said, "I'm strong. I can push."

"No," said the storekeeper. "You are hardly strong enough to push the truck. I'll get some men to come and do that."

Tom said, "I may not be strong enough to push. But perhaps I can do errands. I might carry groceries to people."

So Tom went riding off. He carried pins and clothesline to Mrs. Wood. He carried part of Aunt Susan's groceries to her.

The next day Tom was riding along the old road to Four Corners. He was going there to buy a birthday present.

When Sam stopped to rest, Tom pushed his knees into Sam's back and cried, "Keep moving! Keep moving!"

When Tom got to the store, he said, "I came to buy a birthday present. I did errands to earn the nickels to pay for it."

"A birthday present!" said Aunt Sally.

"Yes," said Tom. "Father's birthday is today. Here are five nickels I earned. Now, please sell me the present."

"What present shall I sell you?" asked Aunt Sally, hiding a smile.

"Oh!" laughed Tom. "I forgot that I haven't told you what I want to buy."

He pointed to a big blue handkerchief that was covered with white stars.

"That's the present I want," he said. "I'm sure Father will be proud of it."

Aunt Sally shook her head and said, "You'll have to pick out something else.

I can't sell that handkerchief for only five nickels. We paid six nickels for it. I have to sell it for more than we paid. That's how a storekeeper earns money."

Tom wondered what to do. He did not have time to earn more money. He would not ask Father to pay for his own present.

"Buy candy for him," said Aunt Sally.

"No," said Tom. "Mother made candy for his party tonight. This handkerchief covered with stars is what I want. It is the only present I really want to buy."

All of a sudden a voice said, "Well! If that's the only present you want, then that's the present you'll have."

Uncle Dick had left his grocery truck in the driveway and had come into the store.

He rubbed his chin for a second or two. Then he picked up the blue handkerchief covered with stars and handed it to Tom.

"You earned this yesterday when you carried the groceries for me," he said. "You didn't think of nickels yesterday. So we won't think of nickels today."

The New Teacher

Today was the first day of school.
It was a busy day for most of the children
living in town or in the country.

Breakfasts were eaten fast.

Mothers waved good-by to children as
they hurried out gates and driveways.

Up Oak Street hurried Patty and Ann,
Molly and Betty. Following the girls
came Joe and John, Peter, Jay, and Bill.

Nancy and Jack Winters followed Tom
and David through Oak Hill Park.

Wags and Skip wanted to follow
the children. But dogs do not go
to school—even on the first day.

This year some of the children had
a new teacher who was not a Sister.
But she was not strange to them.

Everybody had often seen Miss Young
on the playground. Everybody knew
her friendly smile and pleasant voice.

Into the new teacher's room hurried
the children. She smiled and said,
"Good morning, everybody."

The friendly children smiled right back.
The boys smiled as they put away
their caps. The girls smiled as they
found places to sit.

190

"This year you will learn many things," said the new teacher. "I shall teach you more about reading and counting. I shall teach you how to write better.

We have a whole year to work hard. Today we shall take our time and get to know each other."

They said prayers together. Next they sang and the teacher read a storybook.

Then she said, "Let's make pictures."

"What kind of pictures?" asked David.

"Why not make some pictures of me!" said Miss Young with a sudden smile.

Ann whispered to Patty, "I can't do that. I make heads like balloons."

Patty whispered back, "I make noses and chins that are long and pointed."

Miss Young heard the whispers.

She smiled a friendly smile and said, "I'm sure you'll all make good pictures."

Miss Young stood up very straight.

"I'll be quiet. I won't even move while I'm having my picture made," she said.

As soon as all the pictures were done, Molly came up to be Miss Young's helper. They began pinning up pictures.

When Joe's picture was pinned up, he said, "Oh, Miss Young. I didn't part your hair right. I've given you too long a chin, too. You really have a short chin. Please pin up only the best pictures."

"That's just what I am doing, Joe," said the teacher. "I know these pictures are the best that everybody could do."

Miss Young did not look the same
in any two of the pinned-up pictures.

In some she looked like a tall woman.
In others she looked shorter.

There were big chins and little chins!
Long arms and short arms! Fat necks and
tiny necks! Big noses and no nose at all!

In some her hair looked like a black cap.
In others her hair was all puffed out.

The teacher had a proud smile as she
looked at the pictures covering the board.

"They all look just like me," she said.
And strange as it seems, they did!

In each picture she had a big, big smile.

Jay's Pumpkin

"Get your cap, Jay," called Peter.
"Everybody is waiting for us in the park."
Jay turned on one knee and said,
"I must take care of my pumpkin vine."

"We need you," Peter said. "We didn't
have enough boys for a game yesterday."

"Well!" said Jay. "I have to take care
of my pumpkin vine first. I've taken
good care of it all summer. But there
is something the matter with it now.

I'm going to water it and look for bugs
and pull weeds. If I don't, I might not
have even one pumpkin for Halloween."

"I'll help you," said Peter. "You can do the work in a shorter time with a helper."

Peter carried water for the plant.

Jay pulled weeds and looked for bugs. "Growing this vine has been hard work," he said. "But I've been having fun.

I planted five seeds, but only one seed grew. Before long a tiny little plant branched out and ran along the fence.

More and more branches grew until the vine almost covered the ground.

Then lots of big yellow flowers grew on the branches of the vine. And next came little green pumpkins."

After Jay had taken a bug from a leaf, he said, "I've taken very good care of my plant. I've given it plenty of water.

But all of a sudden the pumpkins began to fall off. Every time I touched one it fell off. Now I have just six left."

The next day Jay saw that only five of his pumpkins were left on the vine.

"I hope I can grow five big pumpkins for Halloween," Jay thought.

"I'll give one to my mother for pies. I'll give a Halloween pumpkin to Peter. And I'll keep a big one for myself.

I'll sell the others. I believe I can sell them to the storekeeper."

But one by one more pumpkins fell off. Soon there was only one left on the vine.

It was hardly as big as Jay's head. No matter how much care that pumpkin was given, it never grew any bigger.

On Halloween morning Peter came by.

"I'm going to the grocery store to get our groceries," he said. "The storekeeper is going to give me a Halloween pumpkin."

"Oh!" said Jay. "I had hoped that I would have a pumpkin to give you."

"That doesn't matter," Peter answered. "I'm sorry only one little pumpkin grew on the vine after you worked so hard."

"I was having fun anyway," said Jay. "Even if I didn't grow a lot of pumpkins."

Just then Mr. Green, Jay's neighbor, called from the fence, "Oh, Jay! I hope you'll sell me your big pumpkin."

Jay wondered why Mr. Green had said such a strange thing.

"What big pumpkin?" he asked.

"The one in my yard," said Mr. Green. "One of the branches from your vine reached through the fence. A pumpkin grew in my yard the whole summer."

Into Mr. Green's yard ran the boys. They could hardly believe their eyes. There lay a very, very large pumpkin.

"Oh, what a big joke!" shouted Jay in his loudest voice. "I believe I grew the biggest pumpkin in the country. I didn't even know I was growing it!"

The Christmas Sled

"Now, look, Jane!" said Betty Fox
to her little sister. "What is A for?"

"Apple!" shouted Jane.

"And the letter B?" asked Betty.

Jane shouted, "Ball! And C is for cap!"

Betty was teaching Jane her ABC's from
a book Bill had given her for Christmas.

Betty had been her mother's helper
all afternoon. She had taken care of Jane
while Mother had scrubbed the kitchen
and gone to the store for groceries.

Now Betty was taking care of Jane
while Mother got dinner.

When Jane became tired of ABC's, she got down on her knees to color pictures.

Betty laughed when she saw that Jane had given a woodpecker pink wings.

She had put pink wings on a robin, too.

Betty was having a hard time coloring a picture of a village. She kept going to the window to watch the weather. It was strange weather for this time of year.

It had rained the day before yesterday. It had rained yesterday and today.

Each time Betty looked out, the wet rain was splashing down harder than ever.

"Will this rainy weather ever change?" she thought. "Will it ever get colder?"

If the weather changed and got colder, the rain might turn to snow. Then Betty could slide in the park on her new sled.

Soon Jane said, "Please help me make my new duck waddle." So Betty did.

Back and forth waddled the toy duck. Back and forth waddled Jane following it.

The girls were having lots of fun with Waddle Duck when Father came home.

"Do you believe this weather will ever change and get colder?" Betty asked.

"Yes," said Father. "This wet weather will change. It will get colder soon. I believe it's colder now."

"I hope so!" said Betty. "I want to slide down Oak Hill on my new red sled."

On Friday the weather was much colder. The ground was covered with deep snow.

Now Betty could slide on the sled that Grandmother had given her for Christmas.

Betty and Father went out together.
He tied Betty's warm cap under her chin.

"Look," laughed Betty as she pointed
to feathery piles of snow that covered
the fence. "The fence has caps, too."

"Those are strange caps," said Father.
As he started away, he waved good-by.

"I hope you'll have lots of fun sliding
in the park," he called. "Good-by."

Betty had taken only a few steps toward
the park when Mother ran out to the gate.

She said, "Do an errand for me, dear.
The milkman is often late in bad weather.
Buy some milk from the storekeeper."

Off went Betty to do her errand.

After she paid the storekeeper, she started home with the milk.

Mr. Green waved as she went by.

"Betty!" he called. "I forgot to buy bread yesterday when I got my groceries.

I can't go out in such cold weather. I wonder if you would get some bread for me, please."

"Yes," said Betty. "I'll get the bread as soon as I've taken this milk home."

Betty took the milk home. Then she went back to do Mr. Green's errand.

She bought the bread and was taking it to Mr. Green when Mrs. Brown called her.

Mrs. Brown said, "Jay has caught a cold and can't do my errands. Will you please get a bag of flour for me?"

"Yes," said Betty. "I'll do your errand when I've taken this bread to Mr. Green."

So back she went to get the bag of flour. She worked harder and harder. She was still carrying groceries when Bill called her to lunch.

While the family was having lunch, she told what she had done since breakfast.

"You're a fine helper," laughed Mother. "Your new sled carried lots of groceries. It's a fine grocery truck in bad weather."

Father asked, "Did you slide in the park?"

"I didn't get to slide at all," laughed Betty. "But my grocery truck did lots of sliding on errands to the store.

I'll do my sliding this afternoon."

Old Storybook Friends

The Best One

Once a long, long time ago there was a poor old woman who made beautiful toys.

Since she had no children, she gave the toys to the children of her neighbors.

She did not like to sell the toys. She did so only when she needed money for food.

Each toy she made seemed better than the one she had made before. One day she made a toy animal that seemed almost real.

"This is the best toy I have ever made," she thought. "How sad I should be if some boy or girl did not take good care of it. I don't believe I can ever give it away."

One day there was no food in the house. The old woman knew that she would have to sell some toys if she wanted to eat.

She had given most of her toys away. Now only a few were left.

"I must sell all but The Best One," she thought. "I could never sell that!"

She put all the toys but The Best One in a wide basket. Then she hung the basket over her arm and started out.

She tried to sell the toys to everyone she met. But it was so cold that few people wanted to stop and buy them.

The day grew colder but still the woman went on. A strong wind began to sting and bite her face. It caught her coat and blew it about her so that she could hardly walk.

On she went down the road and over the river. At last she did sell everything.

It was late when she got home. Her face was red from the bite of the wind and her hands hurt from the stinging cold. She sat by the fire to warm herself.

All of a sudden she heard a loud knock at the door. She went to open it.

Outside the door stood Three Wise Men from a faraway country.

"We go to find the little Jesus Who has just come to earth," they said. "We have seen His star and we believe He is God.

We have followed the star over fields and forests and wide rivers.

Look, we carry presents to Jesus."

"Come in and rest by my fire," said the
old woman. "The wind is growing colder.
See how it stings and bites your faces."

As the Wise Men rested, they talked
about the wonderful Baby they would see.

Suddenly the old woman picked up
the small white toy that she loved.

"Take this to the little Jesus," she said.
"Now I know why I didn't want to part
with it. I thought no one was good enough
to have it. Now there is Jesus.

Only the best is good enough for Him."

The Man Who Kept House

Long ago there was a farmer who
believed that his work was too hard.

Every night when he came to his house
on the hillside, he asked the same thing.

"Wife, what do you do all day while
I work hard in the fields?"

"I keep house," his wife always said.

The man would say, "That is so easy!
I wish I had nothing to do but churn butter,
boil porridge, and keep the house clean."

At last one night the man's wife said, "Tomorrow you and I shall change work!"

"Oh, boiling porridge, churning butter, and watching Baby will be easy for me!" said the man. "I'll have a gay time."

The next day the wife went to rake hay. The man stayed in the house.

First he filled the churn with cream.

All of a sudden he remembered he had not seen the baby since his wife went out.

The man was no longer gay. He thought, "How terrible! I hope the baby isn't lost."

He looked for her in the yard. Then he ran down the shortest path to the river.

There he found the baby playing in a boat on the bank of the wide river.

The man caught her up in his arms and hurried back to his churning.

When he went into the kitchen, he saw a mean old pig beside the churn.

The pig had knocked over the churn,
and the cream was running out.

The man stamped the floor and roared
in his loudest voice, "You mean old pig!"

His angry cries scared the pig. It ran
past him and out the door.

He caught the pig and put more cream
in the churn. Then he thought of the cow.
She had not been given water. She had
not had a bite of grass since yesterday.

"This is terrible!" the man said as he
went to get water for the cow to drink.

He carried the heavy churn with him
so that the pig could not knock it over.

The man reached for a rope that hung in the dark well. A river of cream ran out of the churn.

The angry man stamped and roared, but he pulled up enough water for the cow.

After he had given her some water, he started to take her to a grassy field.

All of a sudden he remembered that the baby was all alone in the house.

"This is terrible!" thought the man. "She may fall in the fire and get burned! But what shall I do with the cow?"

The man looked up at the grass that grew on the roof of the house.

"I'll put the cow on the roof. She can get a bite of grass up there," he said.

He put a wide board from the hillside
to the roof to make a bridge for the cow.

She went across the bridge to eat grass.
And the man went back to his churning.

Since it was almost time for his wife
to come home, he had to make porridge.

He filled the porridge pot with water
and hung it in the fireplace. He started
to make a hotter fire to boil the water.

Then he remembered the cow that he
had taken to the roof a few minutes ago.

"This is terrible!" the poor man thought.
"The cow may fall and hurt herself."

He caught up a long, strong rope and
climbed to the roof again.

The man tied one end of the long rope around the cow's big horns. He dropped the other end of the rope in the chimney.

When he got back inside the house, he reached up the brick chimney and caught the rope that hung there. He tied the end of the rope around his leg.

"There!" he said. "This strong rope is tied to my leg and to the cow's horns.

Now she can't fall and hurt herself.

Now I'll make the fire burn hotter and boil the porridge."

Just then the cow fell off the roof!

She hung from the roof by the rope on her horns. There she hung outside the house, crying, "Moo! Moo! M-o-o!"

When the great heavy cow fell outside, the rope on the man's leg pulled him up the chimney. There he hung by his knees upside down above the porridge pot.

The poor man could not get up or down! All he could do was roar in a voice so loud and gruff that he sounded like a lion.

The man's gruff cries got louder
and louder. The cow's angry moos
got louder and louder, too.

"What can this mean?" thought the wife
as she came running. She dropped
her rake and quickly cut the rope.

The angry cow fell down into the yard.

At that very second the wife heard
a sudden great splash inside the house.

She ran in and saw the man. He hung
by his knees in the chimney. His head
was in the porridge pot up to his neck!

Never again as long as he lived did
the farmer try to keep house.

The Three Billy Goats Gruff

Long, long ago there were three goats named Gruff. They liked to eat grass on a hillside across a wide river.

They always took the shortest path to the hillside. And the shortest path lay across a bridge over the wide river.

Under the bridge a mean and ugly troll was often hiding. The ugly old troll had a great loud voice. It sounded just like the terrible roar of a lion.

One day Little Billy Goat Gruff
started across the wide river.

Trip, trap! Trip, trap! Trip, trap! went
his wee feet on the bridge.

"Who is walking across my bridge?"
called the troll with a terrible roar.

"It is I," said Little Billy Goat Gruff.
"I'm going to the hill to make myself fat."

The mean troll stamped and roared,
"No! I'm going to gobble you up!"

"Oh, please don't!" cried the wee goat.
"Wait for Big Billy Goat Gruff to go
over the river. He's much bigger than I."

"Be off with you, then," said the troll.
"Since you are so small, I'll hide here
and gobble up your bigger brother."

After a while the second goat started
across the bridge over the wide river.

Trip, trap! Trip, trap! Trip, trap!
went his feet on the boards.

"Who is walking across my bridge?"
called the troll's terrible voice.

The second goat answered, "It is I.
I'm going to the hill to make myself fat."

"No!" roared the ugly old troll louder
than ever. "I'm going to gobble you up!"

"Don't gobble me up!" cried the goat.
"Wait for Great Big Billy Goat Gruff.
He is much bigger than I."

"Be off with you, then," said the troll.

By and by the third goat came along.

TRAP! TRAP! TRAP! TRAP! stamped his heavy feet across the bridge.

"Who is stamping across my bridge?" called the troll in his terrible voice.

The third goat answered, "It is I. It is Great Big Billy Goat Gruff. I'm going to the hill to make myself fat."

The ugly troll hopped up on the bridge.

He roared in his loudest voice, "Oh, no! I've been hiding since morning, waiting for you. I'm going to gobble you up!"

Great Big Billy Goat Gruff just shook his great big horns at the ugly troll.

"Just try to gobble me up!" roared
Great Big Billy Goat Gruff. Then he
banged right into the ugly old troll
with his great strong horns.

Down into the wide river fell the troll.
Down he fell with the most terrible and
lion-like roar that has ever been heard.

That was the end of the ugly troll!

After that the three goats grew so fat
they could hardly walk. And if the fat has
never dropped off, they are very fat yet.

The First Woodpecker

Long, long ago in a faraway village there lived a sly old woman. She was as sly as the foxes in the woods.

One afternoon she was baking a cake. She believed she was alone in her house. But all at once she heard someone moving.

Turning quickly from the oven, she saw a strange old man standing behind her.

"I have not eaten since yesterday," the strange man said in a friendly voice. "I hope you'll give me a bite of cake."

Smiling a sly smile, the woman said, "Perhaps—when my little cake is done."

When the cake was taken from the oven, the woman thought, "I'll keep this myself. It is much too large to be given away. I shall bake a smaller cake for the man."

An ugly, sly smile was still on her face as she looked at the man.

"You'll have to wait," she said to him. "I'll bake a smaller cake."

The man waited while the sly old woman made a hotter fire. He sat and waited while the smaller cake was baking.

When the cake was taken from the oven, the woman's mouth hung open in surprise.

The smaller cake was so large that she had to touch it to make sure it was real.

"My!" she thought. "This was smaller than my apron pocket when I put it into the oven. Now it's as big as my cap.

I can't give such a fine large cake to a strange man. I'll bake a smaller one."

The mean old woman made a cake that
was smaller than the second one.

"Surely this will be the smallest cake
that anyone can bake," she thought.

While the third cake was baking,
the strange man grew even more hungry.

But when the woman saw the cake,
it was bigger than the one before!

"My!" she thought. "These cakes grow
like magic while they are baking.

This should be the smallest cake, but
it's the biggest. It's much too wonderful
to be gobbled up by this strange man."

The old man rubbed his hands together. Then he reached for the smallest cake.

"Don't touch it!" screamed the woman. "I won't give you even my smallest cake. You'll find plenty of food in the forest. Go there and eat with the wild animals."

"No!" shouted the man. "You, yourself, shall go to the wild woods. You, yourself, shall eat with the foxes and bears.

Since you are too mean to be a woman, you shall be a bird. You shall work hard to find your food in the bark of trees."

The man gave a sudden great stamp on the floor. Then the woman became smaller and smaller and smaller until she was not as high as his knee.

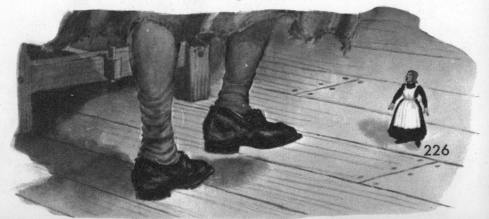

The man gave another stamp. Like magic, wings grew out of the ugly woman's back.

At the third stamp her apron and cap and dress changed to feathers.

The mean and sly old woman had been changed to a bird. It had white feathers for an apron and red feathers for a cap.

The bird lifted its wings and flew off.

That was long, long ago.

Ever since that long-ago time, there have been birds with red caps and white aprons.

These birds are called woodpeckers. They find their food in the bark of trees. Their loud cries are heard in the forest, even to this day.

A Home in the Wild Woods

One morning a long time ago a farmer was looking at his sheep.

"Well, well, my fine sheep!" he said. "I believe that you are bigger than you were yesterday. Soon my wife and I hope to be having you for dinner."

"Pooh!" thought the sheep. "I shall be having something to say about that!

I can fool the farmer. I can hide from him. Then he can't eat me."

When the farmer left, the sly sheep hurried straight to the pen of a lazy pig.

"Hello!" said the sheep. "I hope you know why the farmer feeds you so well."

"I don't know why," grunted the pig as he gobbled and gobbled his corn.

The sly sheep said, "I do. A minute ago the farmer told me. He said that he and his wife were going to eat you. But I'll help you fool him and save yourself.

We can go away together and hide in the deep, dark forest. We can build a house of our own in the wild woods."

"Thanks!" squealed the pig. "Let's take the shortest path to the forest at once."

On the way to the wild woods, the sheep and the pig caught up with two geese.

"Hello!" honked the friendly geese. "What are you doing on such a fine day?"

The sheep said, "We are going to build a house and live together in the woods."

"May we go?" asked one of the geese. "Having a home with jolly friends would be pleasant. Most pleasant, I'm sure!"

"H-m-m," grunted the lazy pig.

"Everybody who goes along must work. Can you cut down trees to make a house?"

"No," said the geese. "We can't cut even the smallest tree.

But we can cover the roof with branches and fill all the wide cracks with leaves. If it gets colder, the house will be warm.

No wind will come in. No rain will come through the cracks and get you wet."

"Oh! Our roof must be covered," the pig squealed. "Come with us to the wild woods."

So the four animals went on together.

Soon they saw a proud rooster.

"Where are you going?" he asked.

"To the wild woods to build a house
for all of us," answered the sheep.

The rooster said, "I hope you'll let me
come, too. When a rooster sleeps under
his own roof, he crows loudest and best."

"H-m-m!" grunted the pig. "Can you
cut down trees and hammer boards?"

"Pooh, pooh!" said the proud rooster.
"The smallest one can't do heavy work.
But I'll do my part. I'll wake you early,
and you'll have plenty of time to work."

The pig squealed, "All right! You can
help even if you are the smallest."

The five animals went on together until they came to the wild woods. There they began to build their house.

The sheep cut down ten maple trees and made boards. The pig hammered the boards together. The geese covered the roof and filled the wide cracks so the house would be warm when the weather got colder.

The proud rooster lifted his wings and waked everybody early each morning.

They were five merry workmen building a house. They were all as happy and gay as could be when their house was done.

What they did not know was that a mean wolf family was living nearby!

Each wolf was sly and mean and ugly.

"Listen, Brother!" the biggest wolf said to the smallest wolf. "Yesterday, I saw some silly farm animals in the forest. I'm going to visit them." And away he went.

The friends saw the sly wolf coming.
They knew how mean a wolf can be, and
they did not want to get caught by this one.

They opened the door wide and waited.

Soon the wolf stepped through the door.
A blow from the sheep's strong horns
knocked him over and rolled him outside.

The pig began to stamp on the wolf.
One goose began to bite his ear and nose.
The other goose caught the hair that hung
down from his chin and pulled it.

The rooster lifted his wings and flew
to the housetop. "Bite him! Bite him!
Bite him!" he squawked.

What a noise! What a loud squawking and squealing there was! All those animals made the loudest squawks and squeals ever heard in the wild woods.

The wolf had such a bad scare that he made no cries at all. He picked himself up and ran home as fast as he could.

"Well!" said one of the wolf's brothers. "You have never paid a shorter visit.

What happened to you? I can hardly tell who you are. You have bites and bumps all over you."

The smallest wolf rubbed his chin.

"Brother," he said, "your chin hasn't a hair on it. Tell me what happened. Did you visit those silly farm animals? Did they drive you away?"

"Yes," cried the scared wolf. "I have been having a terrible time. You should have been there yourself a while ago.

Those big bad animals caught me and stamped on me and tried to gobble me up.

All the time they roared like lions. They called, 'Bite him! Bite him!' "

The whole wolf family was scared!

"Oh, dear me!" said the smallest wolf. "If those mean farm animals are going to stay here, we must move away."

So the wolf family moved at once.

The biggest wolf never forgot his visit. The smallest one always remembered how mean farm animals can be.

And the whole wolf family always remembered why they had to move.

From that day on, the five friends lived together in their home in the wild woods. They were as happy and gay as could be.

TO THE TEACHER

The new *More Friends and Neighbors*, Cathedral Edition, has a total vocabulary of 897 words. Of these, 320 words are new at this level; 231 were introduced at Book Two[1] level; 179 were introduced at Book One level; 107 were new in the Primer; 60 were introduced at Pre-Primer level. Each of the 320 new words in the new *More Friends and Neighbors* is used a minimum of ten times. Each of the 577 words that were introduced in preceding books is used a minimum of five times.

No page introduces more than two of the 320 new words. The first five uses of each new word are bunched for easy mastery, with no gap of more than five pages between any two of these first five uses. At spaced intervals, at least five more uses of each word occur.

The 320 new words used in the new *More Friends and Neighbors* are listed below. The following forms of known words are not counted as new: possessives and inflectional variants formed by adding or dropping *s, d, ed, ing*, derivatives formed by adding or dropping the suffix *y*, variants or derivatives in which the final consonant is doubled before a known ending or suffix. Contractions in which only one letter is omitted and compounds are not counted as new. Letters representing sounds that are not words are not counted. Also, homographs are not counted as separate words; for example, if *tap* meaning "the sound of a light blow" has been introduced, *tap* meaning "faucet" is not counted as a separate word.

The red asterisks indicate 182 words that children should be able to attack independently by applying the word-attack skills learned at this and preceding levels in The New Cathedral Basic Reading Program. The types of analysis that children can use in unlocking these attack words are given in the lesson plans in the *Guidebook* for the new *More Friends and Neighbors*.

WORD LIST

UNIT I	11 ice *	17 hurt	23 . . . . .
	skates *	slide *	24 . . . . .
5 Oak	12 smile *	18	25 valentine
6 waved	13 foot	19 sliding	Betty
7 suddenly	14 lunch	20 sleds *	26 box *
8 horns *	end	21 wet *	paper
9 legs *	15	22 pan *	27 shut *
10	16 arms *	matter	fixed *

238

ACKNOWLEDGMENTS

For permission to adapt and use copyrighted material, grateful acknowledgment is made to the following:

To the author and *Jack and Jill* for "Patty Helps Herself" from "Learning to Ice Skate" by Jo Minner; to David C. Cook Publishing Company and *Dew Drops* for "Fun on the Ice" from "Buffet's First Ice" by Mildred Comfort; to Shepard and Lawrence, Inc., for "Fun in the Snow" from "When the Snow Came" by Mark Francis in Volume I of *Book Trails;* to the author for "Jean's Valentine" from a story of the same name by Mollie McTaggert; to the author for "Bobby's New Shoes" from "One of Billy's Best Friends" by Blanche Heywood in *Junior Home Magazine;* to *The Grade Teacher* for "Which Circus?" from "Donny Goes to the Wrong Circus" by Marjorie Williams; to the Reverend Harold J. Heagney and *Manna* for "Ellen Keeps Lent" from "Little Girl Across the Sea"; to the author for "A Trick for Wags" from a story of the same name by Grace Black; to the authors for "Tom's Wish" from "Billy Goes to Work" from *Farm Stories* by K. and B. Jackson, copyright, 1946, by Simon and Schuster, Inc., and Artists and Writers Guild, Inc., reprinted by permission.

To Charles Scribner's Sons for "The Blessing of the Animals" adapted and reprinted from *Juanita* by Leo Politi; copyright 1948 by Charles Scribner's Sons; used by permission of the publishers; to the author for "Friends for a Farmer" from "Mr. Bob White's Nest" by Robert L. Grimes; to the author and Houghton Mifflin Company for "Sleepy Sam" from "The Drive Without End" in *Calico* by Ethel C. Phillips; to the author and *Child Life* for "Stop and Go" from "The Bureaus with Ears" by Edith Armstrong, copyright, 1929, by Rand McNally and Company; to the author and *The Christian Science Monitor* for "The Kitten That Worked" from "Penny Finds a Partner" by Anne Halladay; to the author and *American Childhood* for "Home Wanted!" from "Charla and the Wrens" by Ruth Kersey; to *The Youth's Companion* (combined with *The American Boy*) for "How Skip Found Joe" from "How Boss Got Home" by Marian Willard; to the author for "Judy and Her Pet" from "The White-Footed Mouse" by Laura Brucciani.

To the author and *Pictures and Stories* for "Billy Ground Hog Finds Spring" from "Sammy Woodchuck Finds Spring" by George S. Lookabaugh; "Mrs. Goose Forgets": adapted and reprinted by permission of Frederick A. Stokes Company, Inc., from *Mrs. Goose of Animaltown* by Miriam Clark Potter. Copyright, 1938, by Miriam Clark Potter; to the author and *Children's Activities* for "The Old Woman's New Hat" from "The Little Old Woman and Her New Bonnet" by Doris Bateman; to *Children's Activities* for "Little Mouse Dances" from "The Dancing

Mouse by Elizabeth Upham; to the author for "The Little Engine" from ' The Pony Engine" by Mabel C. Bragg; to the publisher for "The Most Beautiful Thing" from *Mother West Wind's Neighbors* by Thornton W. Burgess, by permission of Little, Brown & Co.; to the author and *Child Life* for "Second Helpings" from the story of the same name by Elizabeth Ireland, copyright, 1948, by Child Life, Inc.; to the author for "Mr. Hurry Changes Things" from *Mr. Dawson Had a Farm* by R. O. Work, copyright, 1951, and used by special permission of the publishers, the Bobbs-Merrill Company, Inc.

To the author and *Jack and Jill* for "The Two Workmen" from "The Little Workman" by Ruth Anne Korey; to the author and *The Christian Science Monitor* for "Molly Plays a Joke" from "The Baby Who Would Be Himself" by Henry Beston; to the author and *American Childhood* for "Aunt Susan's Clock" from "Why the Clock Held up Its Hands" by Maud Lindsay; to the author for "How Not to Forget" from the story of the same name by Agnes Harter; to *Children's Activities* for "The Birthday Present" from "Billy's Valentine" by Grace and Olive Barnett; to the author and *Jack and Jill* for "The New Teacher" from "Miss Topsy Turvy" by Irene U. Hartwell; to David C. Cook Publishing Company and *Dew Drops* for "Jay's Pumpkin" from "Everybody's Pie" by Dorothy Arno Baldwin; and to the author and *Children's Activities* for "The Christmas Sled" from "Rory and the Red Sled" by Jean Wyatt.

ILLUSTRATIONS

The pictures in this book were made by Connie Moran, Walter Ohlson, Ellen Segner, Keith Ward, Jack White, and Eleanor Campbell.

6 7 8 9 10 11 12 13 14 15 16 17 18 19 20 21 22 23 24 25   61 60 59 58